Descent into Chaos

Robin Cunningham

ISBN (13): 978-0-9988500-0-9 (paperback)
ISBN (10): 0-9988500-0-4 (paperback)

Published by Sphere First Publishing, LLC, Pennington, New Jersey
Printed in the United States of America
Cover design by April Zay

The views expressed herein are those of the author and are recollections that are indelibly imprinted in his memory.

Author's note: *Don't Fence Me In* is a popular American song written in 1934 with music by Cole Porter and lyrics by Robert Fletcher and Cole Porter. Reference to a few of these lyrics in this book is to represent the author's life outlook when he was 13.

In loving memory of

Lora Pauline Cunningham,

Robert Harold Cunningham

and

Sol Levy, M.D.

Circa 1935

Circa 1950

Acknowledgments

This book has been many years in the writing and has benefited from the wisdom and considered advice of a great many people. In a last analysis, however, it is my memoir, an account of what I remember about a critical period in my life.

There are so many people to thank for their counsel and comments that I cannot possibly name them all and hardly know where to begin. So, I will proceed in roughly chronological order. John W. Gibble was an early partner and inspiration. I owe him a great deal. Hanna Fox has worked with me almost from the beginning and we continue to work together. Her advice has been invaluable. I am not the only aspiring writer to benefit from her considerable skills and selflessness. She has become a very good and faithful friend. I am also grateful to the members of the works-in-progress group that she formed, all of whom made valuable contributions.

More recently, Dr. Ayman Ramzy deserves a great deal of credit for nagging me incessantly to finish this book regardless of my protests. He is an excellent psychiatrist and a treasured friend. I also owe thanks to Hakon Heimer and Alden Bumstead who made many suggestions for restructuring the book and who provided insightful editing.

In addition, I want to thank April Zay for the cover artwork and setup of the manuscript. Most especially, I want to thank Arlene Geller for her superb copyediting, tactfulness in converting my initial manuscript into a respectable document, and skillful shepherding of the process of producing this book.

Last, but not least, I thank my wife, Valerie, whose endurance, if not her patience, has been considerable. And, I thank our daughter, Christine, whose life experience, courage and constant support have been an inspiration that has kept me going even in the toughest of times.

I hope this book is a credit to all the above. As they have inspired me, may this book inspire others to tell their stories.

Editor's Note

During my many years as a teacher of creative writing and an editor, I rarely read a writer's work that captivated me from the first time, actually from the first few sentences, as did what would become Robin Cunningham's memoir:

"On Sunday afternoon, April 22, 1956, Satan assaulted me for the first time, penetrating my mind and substituting his thoughts for my own. His voice, my voice, was like a razor slicing into the center of my consciousness. I was thirteen years old."

I was hooked and thus began my fifteen-year stint working with Robin, as he relived the traumatic onset of schizophrenia in order to capture it on paper. Robin has successfully coped with the condition since that memorable day with which he introduces his amazing journey. That it has taken him some fifteen years to produce this memoir is not surprising since he had to be willing to relive those terrifying early years to recreate for us, his readers, both his exterior and interior lives.

From that first sentence, Robin puts the reader into his thirteen-year-old mind as it was assaulted by the voices he heard, voices that violated everything he had been taught to believe. In much the manner that the movie "A Beautiful Mind" and the play "The Curious Incident of the Dog in the Night" put the audience into the interior frenzy and chaos of their protagonists, Robin takes us into his schizophrenic existence.

At the time, 1956, the medications given for schizophrenia, which was considered a severe mental illness, were primitive with unpleasant side effects. Psychotherapy did not usually accompany the medications. Most often, people diagnosed with schizophrenia were hospitalized and overmedicated. Many were institutionalized for life.

Robin attributes his not being institutionalized and being able to live a highly productive, multidimensional life to his exceptional psychiatrist and takes us into his sessions with him. We join Robin as Dr. Levy uses cognitive behavior therapy (before it was defined as such) to teach him coping skills, along with trying out each new and better drug for schizophrenia as it was formulated, during his first phase of living with schizophrenia from April to September of 1956.

Each time I read *Descent into Chaos,* and I read it innumerable times, I marveled at Robin's ability not only to convey to the reader what he went through when he was assaulted, but especially his ability to survive it. I admire his determination to share his story as an example of what is possible and am honored to have played a small part in bringing his story to you, the reader.

Hanna Fox
November, 2016

Foreword

Out of the blue, a man named Robin Cunningham called me one day. He wanted to talk about genetics and mental illness. As the director of a Web project for scientists who study schizophrenia, I get the occasional email from a layperson, but this was my first actual phone call.

Robin didn't want help finding a doctor, a better medication, or a clinical trial. He wanted to know how we could make certain that people with mental illness weren't left out of the explosion in medical genetics research. He also had a sound understanding of modern neuroscience and the potential it holds for truly revolutionary new treatments. I was excited to meet a fellow advocate, and we shared our ambitions about galvanizing the mental illness community.

Then, almost as a side note, Robin mentioned that he had been diagnosed with schizophrenia at the age of 13.

This was a revelation. I had only met people like my younger brother, whose promising life became one of disability and dependency. The few publicly celebrated people like Fred Frese and Elyn Saks, who were successful despite schizophrenia, are far outnumbered by those whose mental illness has left them on the margins of society.

That was only the first of many things Robin revealed to me as we began to work together, not just about the experience of mental illness, but about how to be a strong advocate, how to balance work and the other parts of your life, how to support people in difficult times.

As we became close (brothers from other mothers, I sometimes joked), as we travelled around the country, and started a research advocacy group, I learned a curious thing: If you want to annoy Robin Hugh Cunningham, praise him. Tell him that he overcame a diagnosis of schizophrenia—earning a graduate degree, having a family and a career at the highest levels of American business—because he's exceptional...exceptionally smart, or brave, or strong.

A rare cloud will come over his usually cheerful face, and Robin will tell you that he was instead lucky. That is certainly true. Robin was surrounded by some wise, patient, and innovative people. And he will add that he believes many other people could have full, productive lives if they were to get the kind of treatment and support that he received. I agree, but I still think there is something exceptional about Robin, and maybe it is something that we can provide other people who develop psychosis: resilience.

Researchers are increasingly interested in resilience. They want to learn more than just what make some people become ill; they also want to understand how other people avoid illness, even in the face of incredible traumas. And how do some people persevere and succeed when they do develop schizophrenia, depression, or severe anxiety? I think we can learn from Robin, because he is exceptionally resilient. Maybe he was born with a deep well of this quality, but perhaps his personal strategies and the way he was supported in his early life can be distilled and provided to every young person who follows in his footsteps.

Even after hearing him tell it many times, I find myself mesmerized anew when Robin tells the amazing, harrowing, triumphant story that you are about to read. I hope you will share it with every person you know. Share it with young people who fear that they will have to get off the path of life because of a diagnosis. Share it with the friends and family members who can provide the patient and accepting support that such a young person needs. Share it with everyone else in our society who fears, avoids, and underestimates people with mental illness.

Hakon Heimer
October 2016

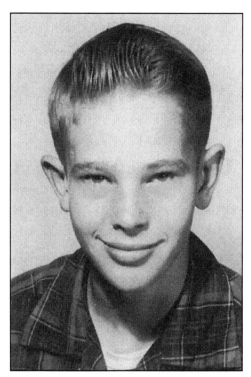

Robin - Circa 1956

Descent into Chaos

April to September 1956

Carl - Circa 1956

1

On Sunday afternoon, April 22, 1956, Satan assaulted me for the first time, penetrating my mind and substituting his thoughts for my own. His voice, my voice, was like a razor slicing into the center of my consciousness. I was thirteen years old.

My Father is God.

Of course, I say to myself, He is God the Father of the Holy Trinity.

No, my father is God.

Alarmed, I realize this thought refers to my earthly father.

What am I doing? Such thoughts are blasphemous!

My muscles tense.

My father is God.

No! No!

His voice goes silent.

I begin to relax. To take stock.

I know the date because my fourteenth birthday is only three weeks away. I've been marking the calendar. I asked for a Remington .22 caliber bolt action rifle so I can go gopher hunting with my brother, Carl, but I'm not holding my breath. Father hates guns.

Father, Mother, and I are on our way home to Spokane. We left Portland about three hours ago, after an extended weekend with my brother at Concordia College where he is preparing to study for the ministry. We're now halfway through The Dalles Mountain Pass that runs along the cliff's edge above the Columbia River on the Oregon side. Father is behind the wheel of our 1948 Packard "woody" station wagon. Mother is at his side. I'm riding in the back seat. Through the blur of the trees flashing by, I occasionally get a glimpse of the river on our left hundreds of feet below.

I look at my pocket watch. It's 3:30 p.m. I'm not happy about having missed Bible class and church earlier in the day. To do so is a sin. Never mind that we're away from home. I could have attended with Carl, but Father insisted we get an early start.

The watch was my grandfather's. Father told me his father bought it when he began working for the railroad. It was a gift from my father on my thirteenth birthday. Father said it is a rite of passage in our family. My grandfather died early, so it was left to my grandmother to pass on to my father. Father had said, "Although I don't plan to die anytime soon, I want to be sure to pass this watch on to you myself. It's a father's duty."

Although it's almost one year since I received the watch, I still don't feel much like a man. I don't feel like a child anymore either. I've fallen between the cracks. I think about the weekend now ending.

My father is God.

The thought re-enters my mind without warning.

Why am I thinking this?

My father is God. If I am with him, it is all right to have skipped church.

A menacing presence is crowding in around me from behind. I can feel its body heat.

My father is God.

I don't believe my father is God! Not the one in the front seat. These thoughts cannot, must not be my own. But they are in my own thinking voice. Who's putting them into my mind?

Sensing great evil in this presence, my fear turns into terror. Despite the heat around me, I'm suddenly cold. Shivers run through me.

My father is God.

If it's Satan, I'm in great danger.

I'm alert now. I feel like a small animal being hunted.

It has to be Satan. But what if God thinks these thoughts are mine? He'll send me to hell.

I want to run for my life, for my eternal life, but I'm trapped in the car and can't see the predator that stalks me.

I'm now sensing a second presence as well. It emerges from the background of my mind. I can feel it, but can't see it. It's reassuring. I've been taught since I started Sunday School that everyone with faith has a guardian angel that God has assigned to protect him or her from harm.

I've been taught that life is a battle between good and evil, between God and Satan. The victor's prize is our eternal soul. I've never been told why God doesn't just get rid of Satan. After all, He is omnipotent.

With the appearance of this second presence, good and evil seem to be in balance again. I'm now a little less agitated. The good, like the evil, stays just out of sight yet close, watching, preparing.

My father is God.

How or where can I hide from thoughts I can't control, thoughts that are not my own, but that are in my mind and thinking voice?

I become agitated once more. My skin burns and my mind races.

I am the Son of God.

This is even worse. I won't think this thought again!

Like a series of electric shocks, muscle spasms jolt me. My skin crackles. My hands clench again and again. I turn my palms down. The backs of my hands are red, as if they've been burned.

How can I escape?

Satan continues to put blasphemous thoughts into my mind. Like a steady drumbeat they pound and pound. My head throbs. It's hard to think clearly.

Please, God, help me. I must stop these thoughts.

Desperate, I challenge Satan. Silently I mouth my words.

Satan, I demand that you stop. You have no right. You must stop…

I am the Christ.

Get thee behind me, Satan.

Afraid I might throw up, I open my book bag and put it between my legs.

My parents, our minister and my teachers have all warned me about Satan for as long as I can remember.

Father's balding head and Mother's graying hair are bobbing and turning as they speak. They're talking about my brother. Five years older than me, Carl is to enter the seminary in less than two years. In our family, being a member of the clergy is the highest honor. My parents are extremely proud of Carl, especially Mother. A son in the ministry continues to be her life's ambition. Two sons in the ministry is her wildest dream.

The last three days at college with the brother I idolized filled me with an eagerness for things to come. We ate hot dogs and baked beans in the student's dining hall and spent Friday night at the symphony. I joked with Carl's roommates. The puns and sarcasm were all a tantalizing adventure.

Yet, the weekend left me greatly troubled. It was the forbidden things that now disturb me: sneaking up the fire escape in the dark with my sleeping bag; hiding in Carl's wardrobe during lights-out inspection; slipping out after curfew to smoke a Lucky Strike; uncovering the hidden case of beer; hearing the cursing and swearing. I am terrified of what my parents would say or do if they knew. They would never understand.

All my life my parents have talked about growing up in the depression, which they regard as close to a religious experience. Their recollections are told like Bible stories, each with a lesson essential to life and death, each passage to be committed to memory. My mother's father had homesteaded in Canada. He had the only well water for miles that wasn't contaminated with sulfur. The land he had obtained was so arid that he sold fresh water and dug graves in the frozen soil of winter to feed his family of eight. My grandfather on my father's side died when my father was twelve years old. My grandmother took in laundry to pay the rent. Every morning before leaving for school my father would cut cardboard to line his shoes because of the holes in their original soles. My father learned the building trades by helping at construction sites when he was a teenager, but he dreamed of becoming a civil engineer. My parents are highly religious, especially my mother, and each in his or her own way has an iron will.

Our parents have worked so hard to send Carl to college, to prepare him for the seminary. But he has been corrupted instead. He is a hypocrite. If they were to find out, it would shatter their dreams. It might even kill them. I can't tell them. But I can't lie to them either. They must never know.

My father is God.

My legs cramp. Straightening them, I fear the muscles in my calves are tearing away from the bone. I grit my teeth and hold my breath. Satan continues to put thoughts into my mind against my will. I pray to God for help.

"Father in heaven…"

I can feel it! Satan is capturing my prayers like a falcon snatches smaller birds in midflight. He's delivering them to my earthly father as if he were God the Father.

I can't allow Satan to do this.

My hands tremble. Covered with sweat, my shirt sticks to my chest and back.

I'm in grave danger. I can't reach the real God!

My stomach turns; acid rises into my mouth. Vomiting is out of the question. I hold my breath. Closing my eyes, I desperately try to convince myself that this is all a bad dream.

My father is God.

No!

I deny each blasphemous thought as Satan forces them into my mind. I try to show God these thoughts are not mine.

Suddenly, I feel Satan inside me. His presence within me is a hot lump. He presses outward against my ribs and my stomach seems to bulge. I'm about to burst.

God help me! Satan is trying to possess me. How can I keep him from entering my heart, from stopping my denials just as he has stolen my prayers?

I must use force as Satan is doing. Each time he tries to enter my heart, I tear at my chest with my thumb and fingernails to stop him. I cover myself with a blanket and try to look as if I'm asleep. I thrash about, but my parents don't notice. With the murmur of their conversation in the background, I wage a desperate battle.

The digging at my chest draws blood. As the wound grows larger, so does the stain on the front of my shirt. I offer my blood and pain as a sacrifice to God.

The hours pass as my war with Satan rages.

It seems like forever before the glow of Spokane's nightlights appear on the horizon. I think of the exciting, and yet disturbing, weekend just spent with my brother. I no longer know him. Perhaps I never did. Clearly, he's not the person I thought he was. I'm now certain of only one thing. The dream of following in my brother's footsteps is shattered.

2

If I can just get to sleep, maybe this nightmare will end.

I get out of the car and head straight for the house. Father calls after me, asking for help with the bags. I ignore him and go straight to the bedroom that I used to share with my brother. I see his half of the room kept tidy by our mother. A tangle of conflicting emotions rises within me. I vow I'll never tell my parents, especially Mother, about my brother's hypocrisy.

I take off my bloody shirt and stuff it under my mattress so Mother won't see it. I'll throw it out in the morning. I put on my favorite pajamas and climb into bed.

My father is God.

No.

I pull the covers over my head. I try to shut Satan out. But he remains within me, trying to force his way into my heart. I scrape my chest again and again, each time drawing fresh blood, adding to that already staining my hands.

Why is Satan assaulting me? I'm not an important person, not like Saint Peter or the Apostle Paul, or even Reverend Voelcker. I'm not like any of the prophets or church leaders we study in school. No one listens to me. So why is Satan spending his time on me? Is there something I don't know?

My father is God.

No.

The bloody shirt hidden beneath my mattress makes me uncomfortable. I toss and turn for an hour. My parents shut off the lights and go to bed. I struggle to fight off Satan for another hour.

Am I cursed? The hot lump in my stomach is beating like a second, evil heart. Will Satan's attacks never end? What if he gains entrance into my heart? Will his evil consume me? Surely he can't continue these assaults forever.

Even with the reading light on, I'm filled with terror. I'm sweating and my hands shake. As I thrash about in bed, Satan increases the pressure within me. I tear at my chest with my bloodied fingers. Bits of skin tear out of the wound and collect under my fingernails.

Something must be done. I can't endure this much longer!

I leap out of bed and turn on the overhead light. I put on my bathrobe and cautiously make my way into the living room. Seeking distraction, I turn on the TV. Taking forever to warm up, its faint, eerie glow heightens my fears. The profile of the Native American head depicted at the center of the test pattern slowly turns and stares directly at me. He looks angry.

I turn to a rerun of the Lone Ranger, but I know he and Tonto can't save me.

The images on the TV screen flash before my eyes like a kaleidoscope. Unable to concentrate, I turn up the volume.

Mother appears in her short terrycloth bathrobe, rubbing the sleep from her eyes. Her frayed cotton nightgown hangs down below the bottom of her robe, dropping to the floor.

I tighten my bathrobe to hide my bleeding chest and hold my bloody hands behind my back.

"Are you all right? What are you doing up at this hour?"

"I can't sleep," I explain as I pace around the room.

Should I tell her anything? Although our daily devotions often warn us about Satan, we seldom speak of him outside of church. I don't even want to say his name.

"Why is the TV so loud? You'd better turn it down before it wakes up your father."

I am the second coming of Christ.

No. I deny this thought. I cannot think such things.

"I thought you were exhausted. You went straight to bed. Your father had to unload all our bags by himself."

Putting her hand over her mouth, Mother yawns.

I am the Christ.

What will Mother do if I tell her Satan is assaulting me, that he is inside me and trying to enter my heart?

"Someone has been putting thoughts into my mind ever since we left Portland."

I held my breath and pinched my forearm in an effort to focus my thoughts.

"Someone has been putting thoughts into your mind? What do you mean?"

She's not angry.

I relax a little, exhaling slowly.

"Someone's making me think thoughts that aren't my own."

"It's just your imagination," Mother says, her tone betraying concern.

She doesn't understand. I can't tell her about Satan, but I can't let her think it's my imagination.

"It's not my imagination. I know because I can't stop it."

Mother studies my face carefully as if she is trying to read my mind. She looks both puzzled and fearful.

"Just put it out of your mind. You're tired and all wound-up from the weekend. Get a good night's sleep and it'll be gone in the morning."

Watching me intently, Mother runs her fingers through her hair, messing up her new permanent.

My father is God.

No! Stop. Please stop.

But Mother and Satan aren't the only ones watching. I sense that second presence again. It's someone or something real.

Is it my guardian angel or a messenger angel direct from God? This would mean that God knows of my plight and will intervene. But the angel remains silent.

"It's not because I'm tired. Someone else is putting thoughts into my mind."

"If you can just get some sleep, everything will be all right in the morning."

There is fear in Mother's voice. She knows sleep won't help any more than a mustard plaster. What's she afraid of? What isn't she telling me? She turns off the TV and insists that I go back to bed.

"We don't want to wake up your father."

My father is God.

I awake with a start.

No. God the Father is my creator.

Despite my terror, I fell asleep sometime in middle of the night.

I am the Chosen One.

No! Please stop.

I open my eyes to find Mother at my bedside staring at me intently.

The blood on my hands and the bits of skin under my nails from the night before are dry. Satan stirs within me. Without thinking I tear at my chest, breaking open the wound.

"You'll stay home from school today," Mother says, as she stares at my wound. She sits very still. I see fear in her eyes. "We'll talk to Reverend Voelcker."

Help at last. Reverend Voelcker will know some special liturgy to stop Satan. He can pray to God on my behalf.

We arrive at the church at precisely 4:30 p.m., after my parochial school classmates have all gone home. Reverend Voelcker greets us and chats with Mother for a few minutes. He then asks her to wait in the reception room, ushers me into his office, and closes the door. He motions for me to sit in one of the chairs facing his desk. He moves to the high-backed executive office chair behind it. On one of the long side walls of Reverend Voelcker's office are windows that are letting in a lot of light; the other is covered with floor-to-ceiling shelves loaded with religious books. I feel as if I'm in a library; that I shouldn't talk.

Reverend Voelcker looks like one of the demons pictured in my grandmother's old German Bible. He's tall, thin and bony, with big ears, a bent nose, and a small patch of long, graying hair that never stays in place. Deep wrinkles twist his face, giving it a snarling look, like a wild beast. I suspect he's hiding some terrible secret.

"Your mother tells me you're hearing voices. Is that true?"

"Not exactly," I say.

"Then, what are you hearing?"

Satan churns violently within my belly. I think he's trying to distract me. He's steadily increasing the rate at which he is putting thoughts into my mind. He's trying to drown out all conversation with Reverend Voelcker.

"I'm not hearing anything. Someone is putting thoughts into my mind."

"So you think someone is talking to you?"

"No one's talking to me. Someone's putting thoughts into my mind in my own thinking voice. He's trying to make God think these are my own thoughts."

I cross my arms across my stomach so that Reverend Voelcker can't see the signs of Satan thrashing about within me. I sit up straight in my chair. All my muscles are stretched tight, my stomach muscles throbbing.

At first Reverend Voelcker looks startled, then annoyed.

"And no one else can hear this voice. Is that right?"

"It's not a voice. Someone is making me think thoughts that aren't my own."

"Is this person putting thoughts into your mind right now?"

"Yes."

I don't tell Reverend Voelcker that the thoughts are blasphemous and that this terrifies me.

Reverend Voelcker leans back in his chair.

"Can you tell me who is doing this?"

I hesitate but then decide I need to tell the truth if I expect him to help me.

"It's Satan."

Voelcker sits bolt upright in his chair, then leans forward, his eyes focus sharply on mine as if he has caught me in a lie.

He spits the words at me.

"Are you trying to tell me that the Devil is putting thoughts directly into your mind?"

"Yes, sir."

"Well, son, I'm sure you just don't realize what you're saying."

"What?"

"You know, don't you, that Satan can be in only one place at a time?"

"Yes sir. I learned that from one of your sermons."

"Remember, he's at war with God. Satan is most certainly quite busy with his diabolical schemes."

"Yes, I know."

What's he trying to say? Everyone knows this.

"Do you really think he's setting aside his precious time to spend with you? Keep in mind that I've been devoted to God's service for thirty-five years and Satan's never found time to spend with me."

Voelcker doesn't believe me. God help me!

A chill runs down my back even as the lump within me seems to grow hotter. The skin on my belly tightens even more. Satan is still within me; his gyrations are painful. This makes it even harder to think clearly.

"I'm certain it's Satan."

I bite my tongue.

Voelcker glares at me for several long moments.

Why does Reverend Voelcker look so angry? Why doesn't he say something?

"You know, Robin, your teacher tells me you're a good Christian, that you're intelligent and that you take your religious instruction quite seriously. He says you're well-behaved and respectful of your elders. He even told me you're a good softball player, that you play second base on the church's junior league team. Is that right?"

"I guess so, some of it anyway."

"He also says that you're planning to enter the ministry like your older brother, Carl. Is this true?"

"I've thought about it."

Satan continues to plague me; the thoughts he's putting into my mind now come one right after the other. The weekend with my brother was an eternity ago. The possibility of following in his footsteps now seems foolish. I no longer want to become what my brother is.

"Of course, I know your father well," Reverend Voelcker continues. "He's been President of the Church Council for the last two years and he's a strong supporter of our school."

"I know."

I know all too well. Father's spends far more time working on the school than with me.

"What I don't understand is why a good boy like you, one with your background, would suddenly make up such a ridiculous story."

Why isn't he listening? He's always preaching about how Satan wants to destroy us.

I am the Messiah.

No!

"It's not ridiculous," I blurt out. "Satan is putting thoughts into my mind right now. I need help and you're not listening!"

Reverend Voelcker frowns.

"Now listen here, young man! This charade is not going to work with me. I don't know what you're after, but don't take me for a fool."

My stomach churns. Acid rises in my throat.

"It's not an act. I'm not making it up. Please, I need your help."

Reverend Voelcker once again glares at me in the most ferocious way.

"I think we should pray," he finally snaps. "You need to ask for God's forgiveness."

Help, at last. Reverend Voelcker will get God's attention. He'll say a cleansing prayer. Soon this will all be over.

"Dear God Almighty, please help your son, Robin. His faith is weak. He is unruly and he tests the patience of his elders. Send him the trial he needs to strengthen his faith. Give him guidance in how to conduct himself and the strength of character to follow it. And please forgive him for his prodigal ways. In the name of Jesus, we pray. Amen."

Reverend Voelcker still thinks I'm faking it! Why won't he believe me?

"Now, Robin, you know that you must repent if you are to receive God's forgiveness. You must stop all this nonsense about Satan putting thoughts into your mind. As I've taught you, repentance involves not only asking for God's forgiveness, but also mending your ways. Without this, there can be no forgiveness."

But I can't stop Satan! That's what I had hoped Reverend Voelcker would do. Without repentance, there can be no forgiveness. He's telling me that unless I can stop Satan's attacks on me I'm going straight to hell.

Having made these comments, Voelcker quickly herds me out of his office.

I tremble violently.

I've been warned about Satan for years, but no one ever suggested he could enter my mind and take over my thinking. Now it's happening and everyone thinks it's my fault, as if I could keep Satan out if I try, if I really want to. Reverend Voelcker's trying to make me feel guilty and ashamed, but I didn't do anything wrong.

My best hope for help in my struggle with Satan has failed me completely. Facing the most powerful of all antagonists, cut off from God, unable to even pray for His assistance, I stand entirely alone.

3

Voelcker is dragging me by my shirt collar down a long, darkened, stone-lined tunnel. There is a light at the end, but it isn't the bright white light that people who are dying are supposed to see on their way to heaven. Instead red, yellow, and orange colors dance as if in competition. A hot wind bearing a foul smell rises and falls with the rhythm of the dancing. The stones lining the tunnel are bleeding from the heat, leaving puddles of steaming water on the roughly hewn stone floor. A large figure standing at the end of the tunnel is silhouetted in the dancing light. I can't make out its features. Suddenly, the creature briefly spreads its wings. I realize it is Satan waiting for me at the entrance to hell.

"Robin is one of yours," Reverend Voelcker shouts. "Take him. He won't repent."

"He's always been mine," Satan replies.

A terrifying scream pierces my ears and echoes down the tunnel. It's my own. I wake up, thrashing about in my bed, illuminated only by the night-light in my room, my mouth wide open in complete silence.

Despite my terror, I once again feel the subtle presence of my guardian angel. He tries to comfort me.

Satan's brutal attacks continue all night; each assault

adding to my torment. Every time I fall asleep, my horrid nightmare repeats. When I'm awake, Satan forces blasphemous thoughts into my mind and presses against my heart, trying to force his way in. My chest aches. My insides churn.

I am the Son of God.

No! Absolutely not.

My fatigue increases each time sleep is promised then snatched away. My muscles hurt from thrashing about in bed. My head throbs. In comparison, the burning pain in my chest is a simple irritation.

Monday's torment turns into Tuesday's agony.

Will this never end? Half asleep, half awake, I'm suspended in a never, never land of anguish.

My clock radio blares, startling me into awareness with the heavy beat of Bill Haley and the Comets singing "Rock Around the Clock."

My mind refuses to focus and my body is numb. Confused and alone, I'm lost in a maze of contradictory thoughts.

Like the images in a house of mirrors, every thought is grotesquely distorted by my growing fear.

How can I possibly force Satan out of my body and my mind?

Mother knocks on my door.

"It's time to get ready for school."

My father is God.

No! Please stop.

The morning at home is always the same. Father gets up at 5:30 a.m. sharp, shaves, showers, gets dressed, and retrieves the morning paper from the front porch. He sits in his recliner and devours the news. Mother gets up at 6:30 a.m., puts on her bathrobe, empties the dishwasher from the night before, and begins preparing breakfast, which is always served at precisely 7 a.m. Mother wakes me up at 7 a.m. and I'm expected to reach the breakfast table by 7:01 a.m.

Each place is set with a plate of two eggs sunny-side up, three strips of bacon and white toast. There is steaming black coffee in white mugs for my parents and milk in a tall glass for me, and for Carl when he is home. A plate with butter and a jar of Concord grape jelly make up the breakfast table centerpiece. In unison, we all recite the same prayer of thanks to God for his bounty and begin eating as we discuss the day's upcoming events. The only variation is when Father hasn't yet finished the morning paper and he brings it to the table with him. When this occurs, no one talks until he puts the paper down. After breakfast, Father always reads a daily devotion and we go our separate ways.

Nausea threatens. The plate of bacon and eggs in front of me is revolting. Father sits across from me in silence, stealing peeks at me over headlines that declare "Devastating Floods Ravage the Midwest."

I am the Son of God.

Absolutely not!

This morning Mother breaks the routine, much to my father's disapproval.

"You're a growing boy," Mother exclaims. "I made your eggs over easy, just the way you like them. Now eat something."

This is a rare concession on Mother's part. She rarely does eggs over easy.

Does she think this will make a difference? She just doesn't get it. No one understands.

"Would you like orange or apple juice?"

"Yes," I stammer.

Satan's frequent thought insertions and his continuing presence within me are making even simple decisions difficult.

Why doesn't he just leave me alone? More and more, my attention is drawn inward. It feels as if I'm shrinking like Alice and becoming invisible like the Cheshire Cat in *Alice in Wonderland*. Will things ever become normal for me again? Trying to imagine my old life at home, I am overcome with homesickness.

How can I be homesick when I'm at home? I'm here as I've always been, yet nothing is the same. I'm trapped in a strange world, surrounded by the familiar sights and sounds of home, but I'm no longer connected. Grief for what I've lost reminds me of the day our cocker spaniel, Skippy, died in my arms. But this time it's a part of me that is dead. I've never felt so alone.

"Don't forget to take a copy of your book report in case Mr. Grimmes asks you to read," Mother says. "It'll guarantee you an A in English."

Why is my mother pretending that there's nothing wrong? Why does she think a good night's sleep and a healthy breakfast are going to help?

I'm living in a strange world looking out at what others do. Satan is no longer a vague concept; he is all too real. Can't others sense this? Why has God allowed this? Is there something God wants me to do? He seems to be sending me messenger angels, or it could be another one of Satan's tricks.

My mother has been dead wrong, twice. Neither sleep nor our minister has been able to drive Satan off. Sending me back to school is a bad idea.

With Satan harassing me all the way, the half-hour drive to school seems to take a lifetime and yet it passes far more rapidly than I want. My hands begin to shake and my skin itches. Our teacher demands our complete attention at all times. How am I going to focus on my studies and still deal with Satan?

Mother stops the car in front of the school entrance and hands me a brown paper lunch bag.

"Be good and study hard," she admonishes.

I am the Christ.

No! No!

My denials require my complete attention. I stumble and almost fall onto the dirt playing field, scuffing my shoes.

A third grader passes me in the hall, watching with eyes wide as I scrape my chest. My skin feels as if it is badly sunburned. The recurring sound of fingernails scraping down a blackboard fills my ears. Trembling and dizzy, I open the door.

My future has been determined since time began.

I am late. Everyone stops talking when I enter the room, turning to look. Staring straight ahead, I make my way to my desk. All eyes follow. I sit down, put my books away and begin to tear at my chest. Fortunately, my desk is in the rear of the room where it's hard for most of the students to watch me closely.

Satan increases his internal pressure on my heart and his verbal assaults are coming more rapidly. Keeping pace with my denials is becoming much more difficult. To avoid distraction, I lean my head back to look at the smooth, white surface of the ceiling.

If the other students find out Satan is inside me, they'll condemn me, just like Reverend Voelcker.

"Why is Robin scratching his chest?" Janice asks, leaning sideways in her chair to get a closer look.

"Maybe he's got fleas," Bill says from the front of the room, his voice cracking.

The entire class bursts into laughter.

Why don't they just leave me alone? Their interruptions are dangerous.

"Quiet down class," Mr. Grimmes scolds.

Mr. Grimmes, our eighth-grade teacher, is tall with wavy, black hair. The girls might have swooned if it hadn't been for his harsh discipline. He's a good athlete and the boys both idolize and greatly fear him. Like Reverend Voelcker, he represents God.

Quick to use the threat of eternal damnation to keep us in line, Mr. Grimmes often makes us feel guilty and ashamed. "Spare the rod and spoil the child" is a scripture passage he quotes daily and applies often.

"As always, at this time on Tuesdays, we'll hear a book report," Mr. Grimmes announces. "Last Thursday, Robin submitted an excellent paper on *Huckleberry Finn* by Mark Twain. Robin, please come to the front and read your essay."

At the sound of my name, uncertain of what had been said, my gaze drops from the ceiling to my surroundings. It appears I am the main attraction in a circus sideshow. Everyone is staring at me. They look as if they can't wait to see what I'll do.

My face flushes, not from embarrassment, but from fear my classmates will disrupt my cleansing rituals. I begin to rock back and forth in my chair.

"I think he's drunk," Bill blurts out.

Once again, everyone laughs.

"That's enough, class," Mr. Grimmes warns. "And Bill, be careful what you say. Slander is a sin."

The laughter stops, but snickering can still be heard.

My father is God. I am the Son of God. I am destined to save many.

No. No!

I'm getting behind with my responses. This is dangerous. I must do something.

In an effort to create a single reply that would cancel out two of Satan's assertions, I begin to shake my head violently with each denial.

I'm getting farther behind. God will think these thoughts are mine.

Sweat bursts onto my forehead. My skin is becoming

badly irritated. The stares of my classmates beat down on me like a hot summer sun, causing my skin to burn. I can no longer ignore the pain. I can feel my face turn red, as if I've been outside in the sun all day.

I claw at my chest. My fingernails catch on the scab covering the wound on my chest. Painfully, a large portion of it tears away. I become queasy.

Suspecting that trouble is coming, the class falls silent. They all turn their head away, but watch me out of the corners of their eyes.

More and more of Satan's evil assertions are slipping past. My soul is at stake and eternal damnation threatens me. I viciously claw my chest again. Blood oozes from the wound. I pray no one sees.

"Robin, come to the front and read your book report," Mr. Grimmes commands.

Why don't they leave me alone? Satan's thoughts are now flooding into my mind so rapidly that I can't keep up with my denials. I try to find a better way of protecting myself. As I shake my head, I begin to softly deny Satan's assertions out loud.

I will save the many.

"No."

I am the Son of God.

"No."

"What did you say, Robin?" Mr. Grimmes asks.

I realize that Mr. Grimmes is certain to misinterpret my no's. The threat of his discipline only serves to increase my fears.

"He said, 'no'." Janice reports.

The other students are now certain I'm in trouble and they don't want to join me. They all stare straight ahead. The room falls silent again.

My hands begin to shake uncontrollably. Hiding them

under my desk, I continue to voice my denials out loud.

I'm falling still farther behind. I must do something more. Now!

"No," I say quite loudly, shaking my head from side to side and stamping my right foot.

"Well, we'll just see about that." Mr. Grimmes speaks as if he were representing an angry God.

"You're in real trouble now," Janice whispers.

Why can't they leave me alone? Satan is gaining the upper hand. My defenses are far more important than the wrath of my teacher. Drops of sweat run down my face. I look straight up at the ceiling again, its blank surface cycling in and out of focus.

"My God," Donna gasps. "There's blood on his shirt."

Mercifully, no one hears her. The blood stain on my shirt is slowly growing larger. Others will soon see it.

I shake my head and tear at my chest.

Mr. Grimmes marches down the aisle and stops next to my desk. Close enough to hear my no's, he doesn't see the blood on my shirt. Grabbing my arm, he roughly pulls me out of my chair.

I am the Savior.

"No," I cry.

I am the second coming of Christ.

"No," I shout.

"Don't talk back to me, young man. These rebellious antics won't work in my classroom."

The people who should be helping me are only making things worse, much worse.

"You're coming to the front of the classroom with me."

With a crushing, painful grip on my arm, he drags me

to the front of the classroom and hands me a copy of my book report.

"Now read, young man."

As I stand at the front of the room, shaking violently and staring at the ceiling, everyone can see the blood stain on my shirt, as well as the tears running down my cheeks. No one moves. Everything around me fades into a shadowy background. Nothing can be heard except my desperate, pleading denials, my recitation of no's.

Robert and Beth - Circa 1908

4

"What happened?" Mother's voice booms out of nowhere.

As I raise my head and open my eyes, my surroundings come fully into focus. The last thing I remember was Mr. Grimmes commanding me to read my book report.

"Well?" Mother persists as we careen along the dirt road leading out of the school parking lot. She always races past the church as if we were fleeing for our lives. A huge rooster tail of dust rises behind us.

My father is God.

No.

I put my hands over my ears.

My head is spinning. I scrape my chest only to discover a bandage.

Who? When?

"I understand you made quite a scene. Is that right?"

Suddenly everything comes back to me in great detail, especially the extreme emotional turmoil. My heart pounds and my mind races.

Made a scene? Does she think I'm just trying to make trouble?

We skid to a stop at Argone Road and are immediately engulfed in a cloud of dust from behind. Slamming the car into first gear, Mother turns right and presses the gas pedal to the floor.

"I'm telling you right now that I don't have time for this nonsense. I've got to go back to the store. Your father wasn't too happy about my leaving. Margaret is out sick, so I'm working at the checkout instead of the office. You're going to have to spend the day alone. If you're going to be sick, you're to stay in bed. You can read, but no TV. Do you understand?"

She wants to put all this behind her. It would be easier for her if I'd just confess to faking it all.

"Robin! Are you listening?"

Thank God we're going home. Away from the intrusions of others, I'll be able to defend myself.

This sounds wonderful until I realize I'll be alone with Satan. What other tortures does he have in store for me? I think about jumping out of the car and running until Satan can't keep up. But Satan is within me. I can't escape him.

"Do you understand?" Mother repeats as she shifts directly into third gear. She rarely bothers with second. I nod my head as the car, engine straining, hurtles down the road.

"Yes. I understand."

When we finally reach home, Mother drops me off in the driveway. Despite all that's happening, she feels compelled to return to the store without delay.

My mother makes decisions like she drives. She'll soon draw her own conclusions about what's happening to me. There'll be no changing her mind then. Decisive action is certain to follow.

God help me.

Moby Dick falls to the floor with a thud that I don't hear. Exhausted, I sleep soundly for the first time in three days.

Mother gently shakes me awake.

"It's time for dinner."

My father is God.

"No!" I shout, thrashing about.

Satan had renewed his attack even before I'm able to open my eyes.

"What is it?" Mother asks in alarm. "What's wrong?" She grabs my arms. Pulling me toward her, she hugs me so tightly I can hardly breathe.

"Satan is after me again," I blurt out.

Despite my confusion, I realize my mistake immediately.

Mother pushes me away to look directly into my eyes. It seems clear that my terror and the mention of Satan are shocking to her.

What will Mother do now that she knows about Satan? And why did he let me sleep? Had he left me for a while?

Mother's face appears to harden with determination.

She's made up her mind.

After dinner, Mother says nothing about homework, but lets me watch *The Lone Ranger*. Satan doesn't disturb me during the entire show, although occasionally I can feel him move within me.

Is he getting bored with me? Will this ordeal end soon?

"Did you enjoy the show?" Mother asks. Her tone is calm and reassuring, but her eyes betray her deep concern. Father, on the other hand, is oblivious, sound asleep in his favorite chair with the evening newspaper in his lap.

"Yes. The Lone Ranger and Tonto caught the train robbers and got the town's money back."

My father is God.

Absolutely not!

I am sent to bed with Satan's blasphemies reverberating in my mind.

Shortly after midnight, I awaken with Satan's thoughts still crowding into my mind. As if I'd been talking in my sleep, my mouth is dry and my throat is sore. I am shivering violently. My pajamas are drenched in sweat. The bed covers are on the floor. Every muscle aches from thrashing around. Satan let me sleep just to prepare me for more of his tortures, to prolong my agony.

No one shall enter heaven except through Satan, for he is the gatekeeper.

No!

Now he's corrupting the word of God. This makes him all the more dangerous.

Deciding I need a glass of milk, I climb out of bed. Much to my surprise, the kitchen lights are on. I hear my parents talking. The tone in their voices makes me approach cautiously. The swinging doors leading from the dining room into the kitchen are closed, but there is a gap I can see through where the doors don't quite come together.

"It would be a terrible mistake," Father exclaims. "Give him a little time to work it out on his own. He'll probably be just fine."

Work what out? Satan is assaulting me. I need spiritual help.

Sitting at the kitchen table, Father is hunched over a cup of coffee that Mother has just topped off. He looks and sounds exhausted. When he tries to take a sip, his hands shake so badly that it dribbles down his chin and onto the table.

"What do you mean, 'he'll be just fine'?" Mother protests. "Your family has always pretended there's no problem, as if that would make it all go away. You've never faced the facts."

What facts? Make what go away?

Mother gets up and moves out of sight. She returns shortly with a sponge and wipes up the spilled coffee, taking the cup out of my father's hands and setting it on the table.

"How can you say I've never faced the facts?" Father exclaims.

"Keep your voice down, Bob!"

My parents never fight. Father always leaves the room whenever mother tries to talk about their disagreements. It's frustrating for her.

"How can you say I've never faced the facts?" Father repeats, his voice strained and bitter. I've never heard him talk to Mother this way.

What's happening? Has Satan gotten to them too?

"Your whole family has never accepted the fact that it carries a susceptibility to mental illness," Mother says. "You're all in denial. The whole family has gone to extremes to avoid the issue. Your twin sister, Beth, lives next door, but you haven't spoken to her in years."

What mental illness? I knew about my aunt Mildred. There are others?

"Denial!" Father says in disbelief. "Ever since my father hanged himself, ever since I was eleven years old, I've gone to bed every night not knowing if I'd wake up in the morning in a private hell like the one that killed him."

What private hell? Killed my grandfather? Was he mentally ill? They must think that I'm mentally ill too!

"Not to worry, Robin. They've got no idea."

Startled, I look around to see who is speaking. I find no one.

Was that just a thought? No, it wasn't in my thinking voice and it wasn't Satan putting a thought into my mind. Someone is definitely talking directly to me in his own voice. It's someone in the room, not in my mind. It's someone next to me, or behind me. But who is it? And where is he? Why can't I see him?

"Who are you?" I whisper.

"Don't be afraid."

"Where are you? Why can't I see you?"

"You can't see me because I don't want to be seen."

"Who…"

"Pay attention! Your parents have no clue about what is happening."

Oh my God, it has to be Satan! He's not only putting thoughts in my mind in my own thinking voice, but he's now talking directly to me!

Satan's voice is soft and comforting, as if he is speaking with the wisdom of the ages, as if he cares deeply for me. But there is also a sharp edge to his voice, as if he could cut my throat with just a word.

What should I do? This is clearly another form of assault. This changes everything. Satan can now interfere in everything I do, both from inside my mind and from outside of it, from inside and outside my body. He's become extremely dangerous.

"Well, you could say something. You could welcome my guidance."

Satan can read my mind as well! He's become a triple threat. How can I possibly stop him now?

My stomach tightens in a knot. I'm suddenly dizzy. My hand goes to my chest.

"I just thought I could be of help."

"I don't want you talking to me," I reply quietly, but forcefully.

"Like I said, they've got no idea?"

"What . . . idea of what?"

"They know nothing of your destiny."

"What destiny?"

"It will become clear to you in time."

"Well, I'm certainly not crazy."

"Of course you're not."

"Then why are my parents talking like they think I am?"

I didn't know that my grandfather had killed himself. Just the thought of this terrifies me. Could this happen to me?

Had Satan talked directly to my grandfather? Did he tell my grandfather to hang himself?

I am staring at my parents in disbelief. Their anger and anguish make them appear to be complete strangers.

"What good does it do to deny it?" Father says. "Will denial help if I get sick? The mental illness in my family has always been obvious enough to those who are close. We've just never advertised."

"But your family waited to seek help for Walt and Mildred until it was too late, until they were too far gone."

Uncle Walt! He died when I was five. He was mentally ill too?

"Of course we tried to hide the fact that my brother and sister were mentally ill. But you know full well we also took them to more than one doctor. And look what it got them. The shrinks couldn't do anything and people found out. They were shunned. Friends suddenly began to treat them like lepers, like idiots. Walt couldn't get a job to save his soul. If you take Robin to a psychiatrist the same thing will happen to him."

They do think I'm crazy! These aren't my parents. Reverend Voelcker and Mr. Grimmes might turn on me, but my parents never would. Satan has gotten to them!

Father picks up his cup to drink, but he spills even more coffee. Without comment, my mother wipes it up with her sponge.

"The doctors might be able to help," Mother persists.

"Not likely," Satan says in a soothing voice. "Be careful here, Robin. Don't let them talk you into doing anything stupid."

"Like the doctors helped Walt and Mildred?" Father shoots back.

"Bob, keep your voice down!"

"They said the brain surgery would help," Father says quietly, his voice breaking.

Was this the operation Mildred had? Uncle Walt had one too? My mother wants me to have brain surgery!

"But they didn't know what they were doing," Father continues. "Do you want them to experiment on our son? My brother and sister may not have had much in life, but the doctors managed to destroy even that. I won't let that happen to Robin."

"Listen to your father. He knows the truth of it. I can't recommend any involvement with doctors."

"Why should I listen to you?"

"I'm the only one telling the truth," Satan insists. "I'm here to help you."

"Please stop talking to me. This is confusing. You're not helping."

Why does Mother want to take me to a psychiatrist if the doctors destroyed Walt and Mildred? And why does Father think I can defeat Satan on my own? They're both wrong.

"And you think mental illness won't destroy Robin's life?" my mother continues.

"If you take him to a psychiatrist, you'll be taking a

terrible chance. He's a bright boy, but people will conclude he's weak or lacking in character. They'll never give him a chance. He'll start life with two strikes against him."

Until now, I couldn't imagine life without my parents' love and support. Now their conversation is almost as terrifying as Satan's.

"Your parents haven't a clue."

"Stop talking to me!"

"Your destiny has been determined."

"We may not have a choice," Mother says.

"There's always a choice," Father counters. "The hard things in life build character. Robin's problems will make him all the stronger if he can work it out in his own way."

My parents are playing into Satan's hands. I don't need medical attention. And I can't fight off Satan by myself.

My heart is beating out of control. My head feels hot, as if I am running a fever. Breathing slowly and evenly, I try to calm myself.

"I'm glad you can see the truth. Avoid doctors at all costs."

God, please make him stop.

"You and I can work this out together. Dump your parents and all your other relatives. Just follow my lead."

"No."

"Are you worried about Robin's quality of life," my mother asks, "or that others might discover you're the source of his problems?"

Struggling to regain his composure, Father sits up straight and wipes his eyes.

"That's not fair. No matter what happens, Robin is my son and I'll always stand by him."

"That's what scares me. You'll stand by him but do nothing. Hoping for the best you'll just watch as he sinks. With or without your permission, if he doesn't show real signs of improvement in the next couple of days, if he doesn't seem to be working it out on his own, I'm taking him to see a psychiatrist."

I vow I'll never go willingly.

5

"Oh, give me land, lots of land / under starry skies above," Gene Autry croons. "Don't fence me in."

I just want to be free like the song demands.

"Let me ride through / the wide-open country that I love," I harmonize, "Don't fence me in."

"Well then, don't let them fence you in," Satan interjects. "Take off. Get out of Dodge."

"I can't leave. I have nowhere to go."

"I can help you with that. But you need to get out now."

I've been playing this song and other favorites in the seclusion of my room for two days.

Mother stopped trying to prevent me from tearing at my chest. Each morning and evening she appears to apply a fresh dressing to the wound.

Satan is still trying to force his way into my heart. He applies a slow but steadily mounting pressure all across my chest. I resist by taking deep breaths. After each breath, I balloon my chest by holding the air in my lungs and push outward to counter the pressure he applies. Whenever I exhale, he makes a pinpoint assault at the site of my chest wound that results in sharp stabbing pains. This effort to protect myself, along with the pain, is exhausting.

I am now certain Mother plans to take me to the doctor.

"You need to get out now," Satan says again. "They're going to operate on your brain."

They're going to operate! Will it change the way I think? Will I remember anything? What makes them think they can cut Satan out of my brain? He'll just take up residence in what is left. They are going to destroy me!

"You're right. They can't cut me out. You belong to me."

"No, I belong to God. You can't fool me."

Already I mourn my passing. Fear is all that keeps me from running. Being unable to escape either Satan or the doctors, like a prisoner on death row, I am terrified of what is surely about to happen, yet I agonize over the wait.

If they operate on my brain, will I become a mental vegetable? What would it be like? Will I become stupid or just not care anymore? But maybe it will kill the pain. Satan may give up on me if they operate. Maybe this is what happened to Uncle Walt and Aunt Mildred.

Playing my melancholy songs, I wait in my solitary cell for a pardon that will never come.

These same songs are still playing in my head as we drive down Division Street and into downtown Spokane. My terror grows even more as we walk to the Paulson Building where Dr. Levy, the psychiatrist with whom my mother has made an appointment, has his office. Mother has to all but drag me into the elevator and out again on the seventh floor. The building is old and the poor lighting in the hallways heightens my fear. As we walk past a series of doors on our way to suite number 711, I wonder if it's possible to house dungeons this far above ground level. Finally, Mother pushes me forcefully through the door and into the doctor's office.

Looking around the waiting room, much to my surprise, I see no signs of the insane. There are no straightjackets or chains. No one is talking to the walls or rolling around on the floor. Unlike the movies, no one with wild eyes is sitting in the corner drooling. There's only a small boy about seven years old sitting in the corner reading a Superman comic book.

I am the Son of God.

No! That's blasphemy.

Mouthing my denials and tearing at my chest, I begin to pace around the room. Mother promptly directs me to a chair under the windows and thrusts an issue of *Game Fishing* magazine into my hands. She takes a seat on the opposite side of the large, square coffee table in front of me.

The little boy soon appears at my side. Looking first at the copy of the magazine, then at me in wonderment, he waits politely for me to notice him.

"There's nothing a doctor can do for you," Satan continues his comments with a note of irritation in his voice.

"The doctor can destroy my mind. He can give me pills or operate on me. He can experiment on me and turn me into a vegetable."

"You can still run. Tell your mother you need to go to the bathroom and take off."

"And you'll come with me, right?"

The boy could wait no longer.

"Do you know that your chest is bleeding?" He seems genuinely concerned.

I don't say anything.

"Does it hurt?"

"Who is this little fool? Get rid of him."

Satan makes no attempt to hide his frustration. His voice is now hard and sharp like a straight razor.

"Are you a fisherman?" the boy asks, looking again at the issue of *Game Fishing* in my hands.

"Answer the young man," Mother says.

I don't respond.

"Don't be rude," Mother exclaims. "Answer the boy's question."

I am the second coming of Christ.

"No!"

"Robin!" Mother demands, "Mind your manners. Tell him you're a great fisherman."

I must have spoken out loud. What's happening?

"No?" The little boy persists.

I am a fisher of men.

"No, I'm not. Jesus is a fisher of men."

"I'm asking if you're a game fisherman," the boy says. "Who said anything about fishing for men?"

Did I just say that Jesus is a fisher of men out loud? Am I a fisher of men? Is God trying to tell me something?

"Robin. What's gotten into you? Tell the truth."

"Yes."

"Yes, what?" The boy persists. "Are you a game fisherman or not?"

I will save the many.

No. I can't.

"Yes, I'm a freshwater game fisherman."

"I thought so," the boy says.

I am destined for greatness. I don't need God's assistance.

"No. It isn't true."

"What?" The boy asks.

"God, please help me."

"Are you a game fisherman or not?" The boy persists.

"Yes. I'm a freshwater game fisherman."

The boy's eyes light up with admiration and his smile broadens.

"Ditch the little brat. We have to talk."

"I'm a fisherman too," the boy says.

"Dr. Levy is a quack," Satan says. "They're all quacks."

"I'll bet you've caught lots of big fish," The boy exclaims.

"Yeah, I've caught some big fish."

"I thought so. You look like a ..."

"Did you hear me? Ditch the little twit. We've got to talk. Now!"

"I caught a big fish once," the boy brags. "It was a perch. Do you fish for perch?"

"What?"

Am I to ditch the perch? No, I need to ditch the little twit! Do I fish for men? No, I don't fish for perch. Then what do I fish for?

The boy is confusing me. As my words and thoughts become more and more jumbled, matched and mismatched, it becomes harder for me to follow my own thoughts and carry on a simple conversation.

But why am I becoming so confused? What is happening to me?

"Forget about the little brat. We need to talk about Dr. Levy."

"No, I don't fish for perch," I reply, "only freshwater game fish."

"I thought I told you to get rid of the little fool."

"Look kid, I don't have time to talk right now."

The boy's chin and shoulders droop.

"Robin!" Mother exclaims. "You're being rude!"

Mother doesn't understand. Satan is confusing me with his constant interruptions. Why does she refuse to believe that Satan is talking to me?

"Is she your mother?"

"Yes."

"Robin! Time is running out. We must talk."

"My mom is in Dr. Levy's office," the little boy whispers. "We come once a week, you know. Mom cries a lot."

"Dr. Levy's going to screw you all up just like your father said."

"I don't know what he's going to do."

"He's a shrink, isn't he? God put shrinks on this earth so he has a way of messing people up."

"God doesn't mess people up."

"Where have you been all your life?" Satan asks.

"You're wrong."

"I'd like to catch a big, freshwater game fish," the little boy interjects. "Would you show me how?"

"You have to be a man to go for game fish. Your dad should take you fishing."

"If this whole business with the doctor goes badly, you'll have no one but yourself to blame."

"My daddy lives in New York now, wherever that is. I

hardly ever see him."

The boy stood silently for a long moment, staring at nothing.

"Don't you go fishing with your father?" The boy finally asks. "I thought you said everyone goes fishing with their father."

Like a slap across the face, catching me completely by surprise, the boy's comment stings. Satan was right about what to do with this little brat.

"Look, you little twit. I haven't got time to waste talking to you. Why don't you …"

The door to Dr. Levy's office opens and the boy's mother emerges.

Hurt and disappointment spread over the boy's face. Running to his mother, he looks back at me with tears running down his cheeks. His mother's eyes are red as if she has been crying. She gathers her belongings and heads directly for the exit. Her son follows. As the door closes behind them, the little boy looks back at me.

"You're just like my dad," he says.

I'm ashamed.

Much like me, with no father willing or available to teach him about the sport of fishing, the boy had turned to someone else, me.

My father is God.

Not this again. Please, God. Make him stop. Please…

My cruelty is quickly forgotten.

"Remember, Dr. Levy makes his money by conning people. If you cooperate, you may find yourself a resident at Eastern Washington State Hospital—just like your aunt Mildred."

Mother goes in first.

Satan continues to harass me as I sit in the corner of the waiting room. Mother reappears in about ten minutes and takes a seat. Dr. Levy appears at the door of his office and motions for me to come in.

I'm convinced of two things. I'm not crazy and there's nothing this Dr. Levy can do for me.

I enter his office cautiously, taking a chair in front of his desk. Foul smelling cigar smoke hangs in the air like a heavy fog. Dr. Levy is short and stocky with wavy, grey hair. His wrinkled suit is covered with spots and tiny burn holes from fallen cigar ashes.

The doctor sits behind his desk and knocks an ash off the end of a fat, green cigar. It misses the ashtray, falling onto the glass covering the top of his desk.

My first impression is not reassuring.

But then he speaks to me.

"I understand that Satan is talking to you."

"What?"

"I understand that Satan is talking to you."

Wait a minute! He didn't say that I *think* Satan is talking to me or that I *think* I'm hearing voices that aren't there. He seems to accept the fact that Satan is talking to me.

"Beware! This is a trap. He's pretending that he believes you."

"But you are talking to me."

"How's he supposed to know that?"

"I don't know! But I think he believes me."

Satan now begins to press hard against my chest again. The pressure makes my stomach bulge. Nausea threatens.

"Stop, please stop."

"I'm warning you. It's a trap. Next thing you know, he's

going to experiment on you just like your dad said."

"You're trying to possess me."

"I'm trying to protect you."

"I think Dr. Levy believes me."

"Don't be a fool."

"Yes, Satan is talking to me."

"Is he talking to you now?" Dr. Levy asks.

"Yes."

"I thought so," Dr. Levy says, leaning back in his chair.

How could Dr. Levy possibly know this?

"Is he communicating with you in any other ways?" Dr. Levy asks.

"He started out by putting blasphemous thoughts into my mind. He's been using my thinking voice to make God think that these are my own thoughts. No one seems to understand the difference. The difference is important."

"You're right. It is an extremely important difference."

I note a slight German accent. I make a mental note of precisely what he's saying and exactly how he's saying it. Does he alone believe what I've been telling everyone, or is he trying to con me as Satan suggested?

My father is God.

No.

I am the second coming of Christ.

This is not true.

I will save the many.

I cannot even save myself.

I squirm in my chair.

Dr. Levy is watching me intently.

"Your mother tells me that you've injured your chest."

"Your destiny is with me," Satan insists. *"Don't do anything this quack says."*

"What you offer is eternal damnation."

I'm too busy to reply to Dr. Levy.

I will save all of mankind.

No, God has already saved us all.

Dr. Levy gets up from his desk and goes to the door.

"Mrs. Cunningham, you may come back in."

I am the second coming of Christ.

No! It's a lie. I won't think this way.

My mother sits down in the chair next to me, reaching out to take my hand.

"Among other symptoms, Robin is experiencing thought insertions and is clearly hallucinating. I'm certain he is terrified and completely exhausted. My recommendation is to hospitalize him, but only briefly, just long enough for us to get him stabilized."

Mother jerks to attention.

"I won't put him in Eastern State Hospital. He'll never get out. His grandfather and uncle died there, and his aunt is there now. It would be a horrible place for a child."

My mother's voice, marked with the sharp, jagged edge of fear, registers with me. I try to listen despite Satan's demands.

"I know," Dr. Levy replies. "At one point, when I was medical director at Eastern State, I treated both his uncle and his aunt. No, I won't send him there. There's a private hospital here in the city that would be much better. It's more like a small resident hotel staffed by experienced professionals. He'll get a private room and personal attention, and I'll be able to check on him daily."

"What he means is that every day he'll stop by to see how his guinea pig is doing."

Is Father right? Will Dr. Levy experiment on me?

"Don't be unduly swayed by the experiences of his grandfather, or his aunt and uncle," Dr. Levy advises. "A new medication has been developed that may help Robin. It could make a considerable difference with someone so young. As I said earlier, the fact that you have brought Robin in to see me just five days after his troubles began could also be important. I'm going to give him a dose of the new medication now and then I want you to take him directly to the hospital. I'll call ahead so they'll know you are coming. You can get his things, pajamas and the like, later today or tomorrow."

Dr. Levy opens a desk drawer and takes out a bottle of pills, removing one. Filling a clean glass with water from the pitcher on his desk, he hands the glass and the medication to me.

"Remember, he's a shrink. He's not to be trusted. I wouldn't take the pill. It's almost certainly an experimental drug. He probably doesn't know what it'll do to you."

I look at the large pinkish-orange pill.

"If you take the pill, you'll be making a bad mistake."

I hesitate, struggling. What will happen to me if I take this pill? I remember what my father said about Walt and Mildred. Will this pill, which they never received, actually help me or will I be part of some terrible experiment like they were? If this pill doesn't help me, it will surely destroy me. I've been warned.

But then, Dr. Levy's first words are still ringing in my ears. "I understand that Satan is talking to you."

Dr. Levy is the only one who seems to believe that I'm telling the truth. He hasn't passed judgment on me. He hasn't made me feel ashamed or guilty. He's the only one who doesn't seem to have expectations of me. In the time of my greatest need, he's the only one who's taken me at my word.

I put Dr. Levy's pill on my tongue and wash it down with a drink of water.

Mildred - Circa 1917

6

I wake up with a start. Jerking to a sitting position, I look around, my eyes wide open. My surroundings are in sharp focus.

I feel good, rested and strong. Why? What happened?

Looking out into a strange bedroom, I remember my meeting with Dr. Levy the day before and my entry into the hospital.

Yes, this is the hospital and the room.

Then it strikes me. I shudder with the full force of it. Silence! It's wonderful and powerful. Satan is no longer inserting blasphemous thoughts into my mind. I no longer feel the pressure on my heart, no stabbing pains. The harassment, the torture has ended. Denials are no longer required. It's over!

My spirits soar. Dr. Levy's big, pinkish-orange pill is working. My mother had been right.

As a warm feeling of relief spreads over me, I think of Aunt Mildred and the horribly crowded and depressing quarters in the state hospital. Why was she sent there instead of here? Could Dr. Levy's pill have helped her too? I relive a day when Mother and I visited her two years earlier. I am there once again. I see, hear and feel everything.

Everything about Eastern Washington State Hospital disturbs me. The buildings are gray, both inside and out, and run-down. Mildred's ward is badly overcrowded. My aunt shares a bedroom, actually just an alcove, off the main hallway, with two other women. Their beds and nightstands are side by side with a large cardboard box for clothes at the foot of each bed.

Mildred is dressed in a gray, wool skirt and red, cotton blouse. She is thin and appears to be exhausted. She doesn't look at all like the pictures I had seen in our family album in which she seems young, healthy and happy.

Phyllis is one of Mildred's roommates. She's old, tall, and slender with stringy, blond hair. Curled up into a ball, with feet tucked under and arms around her knees, she's sitting on the foot of her bed rocking back and forth. Talking rapidly, she never turns to face us. Hiding behind Mother, I watch her closely.

"I figured out that they cook patients and serve them in the staff dining room," Phyllis says. "Sometimes they don't even wait until they're dead. But I'm too tough. That's why they haven't let anyone visit me for seven years, wait…maybe it's been seventy. They don't want anyone to find out."

I wonder if Phyllis is contagious. What if all the patients here are contagious?

I want out.

Fortunately, Mildred, Mother and I soon leave for a walk along the brick pathways that crisscross the hospital grounds. An earlier rain left puddles everywhere.

"Aunt Mildred, why do you stay here with these crazy people?"

My mother tries to silence me, but isn't quick enough.

"That's all right," Mildred says, looking at my mother. "I stay here, Robin, because they won't let me out. They say I've lost all my inhibitions. But the real reason is that all the doctors want me, but I won't do it for them. Besides, I've got nowhere else to go."

"Do you mean they can keep you here just because the doctors want you? What do they want you for?"

"I'll explain later," mother says quietly.

"Please, Mildred. You said you wanted to see Robin, but I can't bring him here if you're going to…"

"They say I talk this way because of the surgery. The idiot doctors cut my brain in half. Then your lousy brother divorced me to marry that slut, Beatrice. She's raising my children, my own flesh and blood, while I sit out here and rot. My husband…I mean my ex-husband, bless his frigid soul, won't even bring my children to see me. None of the women here get to see their children."

"I know that it must be hard," my mother says. "But…"

"You know nothing," Mildred snaps. "You're sitting home nice and pretty with your kids right there. You haven't got a clue, so don't patronize me."

After a brief but uncomfortable silence, we begin to walk again. It soon starts to sprinkle lightly. Darker clouds are rapidly approaching. We take shelter in the patient commissary just as a heavy downpour begins.

My mother buys stationery and stamps for Mildred and a banana split for each of us.

My aunt talks about how she misses her children. I think about how I would miss my mother if she were in this horrible place. Mildred's situation makes me sad. Her living in this drab and forsaken place seems to be some terrible mistake. She's thin and obviously unhappy but she doesn't look sick to me.

When it's time for us to leave, Mildred hesitates and then, almost as if she were doing something forbidden, gives me an awkward hug.

"You're like my own," Mildred murmurs. "Thank God your mother brings you to see me. You're now my fourth child, my third son. God bless you and God bless your mother."

I hug her back, no longer caring that she might be contagious.

My remembrance ends abruptly. I am in my hospital room. A woman in her thirties with short, blonde hair appears at my bedroom door. She's wearing a white blouse with frills down the front and a burgundy-colored skirt. She reminds me of actress Debbie Reynolds.

"Good morning. My name is Beth. I'm your day nurse. How do you feel, Robin?"

Her voice is soft and her smile reassuring.

"I feel great. Can I go home now?"

"You'll have to discuss that with Dr. Levy."

"Well, I need to get out of here. The school year is almost over and I'm graduating."

"Do you think you feel well enough to go back to school?"

"Sure. I feel just fine. I can't miss my graduation."

"Your graduation's certainly important. But remember, you've been through quite a lot."

Then she adds, more to herself than to me, "Certainly more than most people could handle."

"It's not only graduation. Our church softball league is supposed to start a couple of weeks later. I'm starting on the men's team this year. I'm going to try out for second base, so I've got to practice."

"How long have you been playing softball?"

"Since I was eight. That makes five years now."

"I'm impressed."

"It's no big deal," I say, flattered all the same. "And Carl will be coming home from college for the summer soon."

"Is Carl your brother?"

"Yeah, he's studying for the ministry."

"You must be proud of him."

"The whole family is proud of him."

"Well, you definitely have a lot of plans, but you might need to take it easy at the start. You've been here for a while. It all depends on what Dr. Levy says."

"What do you mean, 'I've been here for a while?'"

"Don't you remember?"

"Remember what?"

Beth laughs softly.

Why did she laugh? Uneasiness washes over me.

"I didn't think you would. What would you guess? How long do you think you've been here?"

"That's easy. I checked in yesterday afternoon, on Friday, so this is Saturday. I've been here overnight."

"Well, not quite. Believe it or not, you've been here over the weekend. It's now Monday morning."

That can't be right. A whole weekend couldn't have simply disappeared.

"You're kidding me."

"No, Robin. You've been here three days."

"Why don't I remember?"

"You've been sedated."

"Why?"

My father is God.

The clear focus I have on my surroundings dissolves into a blur. I begin to shake violently.

I am the Son of God.

No, this is not true.

I tug at my chest with my fingernails.

"You don't want to start that again now that your chest is

finally beginning to heal."

Beth takes my hand in hers and holds it until I pull away a moment later.

I tear at my chest.

"It's a little early for your medication," Beth says, her voice calm. "But then we're still trying to get you on the right dose. I'll see if I can get something for you."

Beth leaves.

Now I'm alone with Satan and truly frightened. He's obviously pleased with the shock and fear his sudden return has caused. The moment of his reappearance has been carefully chosen to produce the maximum damage. No doubt remains. His real goal is to completely separate me from God, to drag me down into hell, perhaps the hell I'd dreamed about.

My father is God.

Stop.

All around I hear fingernails scraping down a blackboard, the sound shredding my nerves. My muscles tense and my skin tightens as if I'd stepped into an ice-cold shower. Touching anything burns like dry ice. All my nerve endings seem frozen and, at the same time, on fire.

I am the Son of God.

No!

I thrash about on my bed, rolling violently from side to side and pounding on the mattress with my fists. Kicking the blanket and top sheet onto the floor, I throw my pillow across the room. I bang the back of my head on the wooden headboard. The sharp pain accompanying each blow provides a brief distraction.

My father is God. If I worship him, all this agony will stop.

"No," I cry out loud. "I won't."

If I worship my father, this torture will end.

"No, I can't."

Beth comes back with a glass of water and a white paper cup containing a single pill.

"Here, Robin. Take this. It'll make you feel better."

I swallow the pill with a sip of water and leap out of bed.

"Robin? Robin! You need to stay in your room." Beth moves quickly to block the doorway leading into the hall. "Why don't you sit in your lounge chair?"

"No," I cry. I can hear the terror in my voice.

I realize for the first time that failure to deny Satan's blasphemous assertions creates a mysterious and universal imbalance in nature.

I begin to march back and forth at the foot of my bed, pounding my fists on my hips with each step. Finding some relief, I immediately adopt this new defense, which comes with an urgent need for symmetry.

Any imbalance in my physical movements is also damaging. When I hit myself, the number of right-handed blows must equal the number of left-handed blows. When pacing, an equal number of steps by both feet is important. An equal number of steps in each direction is also required.

Beth tries to console me. Despite her attentions, escape is essential. Leaving this world behind as I had left Mr. Grimmes' classroom, I withdraw, rapidly becoming less and less sensitive to my surroundings. Beth watches intently, her concern apparent, as I make my escape.

Beth's voice comes from afar.

"How are you feeling?"

"What?"

I try to focus.

"Are you feeling better?"

Her question is now clear.

"Yes. I think the medication is helping."

I find myself sitting in my lounge chair.

"How long have I been sitting here?"

"It's been about an hour."

Although my muscles ache and I am emotionally exhausted, I'm no longer distraught. Still, Satan continues to harass me.

My father is God.

I try to get out of my chair, but my legs are rubbery.

"Why don't you just stay put and rest for a while."

"Beth told me that things got a little rough this morning." Dr. Levy says.

I don't respond.

"She says you left us for about an hour. She was worried about you."

"She doesn't understand."

"No, I suppose not. But then, she didn't do anything to make matters worse, did she?"

"You mean like Mr. Grimmes?"

"Your mother told me about the episode with your teacher and your book report. I don't think Beth understands what happened, so she naturally worries about you. But yes, I mean like Mr. Grimmes. Beth didn't do anything like that, did she?

"No."

"Well, that's good. And you're right. Beth, like your mother, doesn't fully understand what you're going through.

Perhaps they never will. That's not surprising. Few people do, you know."

"But you understand, don't you?"

"Perhaps I do, at least a little more than most people."

Dr. Levy is being modest. Somehow I know that he fully appreciates the nature of my terror.

Neither of us speak for several minutes.

"Well, if there's anything you need, just let Beth know, and we'll take care of it."

Dr. Levy gets up to leave.

"Dr. Levy?"

"Yes."

"Does everyone think I'm crazy?"

"Does it matter?" He asks, sitting down again.

"No."

"Then why do you ask?"

"Were my uncle Walt and aunt Mildred crazy?"

"Why do you ask about them?"

"I'm not crazy. It would be a mistake for anyone to think I am."

"Why does that concern you?"

"I don't want to end up in the state hospital like they did. I've visited my aunt there. It's a horrible place."

You don't have to worry. You're not going to end up at Eastern State. I promise. You and I will make sure of it."

"Good. It wouldn't be right."

Again, we sit in silence.

"Well, I've got to get back to my office," Dr. Levy finally says.

He gets up to go.

"Dr. Levy?

"Yes?"

"Do you think I'm crazy?"

"You've told me that you're not and that's good enough for now."

7

"They're just plain folk like everybody else," Beth remarks. "They don't bite, you know."

Three days earlier Dr. Levy gave me permission to visit the patient lounge. I'd stuck my head out the door of my room once, just long enough to look down the dark and gloomy hall with stained wallpaper and a smelly carpet.

"I don't want to visit with anyone."

"But you might make friends. Why don't you give it a try?"

Every time I think of walking down the hall to the patient lounge, my breath comes in hard, short gasps. My legs grow weak as if I'd just run ten laps around the playing field. I feel Satan stirring within me, pressing hard against my heart, seeking entry.

Satan, my constant companion during my waking hours, continues to put a steady stream of his thoughts into my mind and in my own voice, making it necessary for me to deny each and every one. He warns that mixing with crazy people might contaminate me.

"What can it hurt to just go down to the lounge for a short visit?" Beth continues. "I'll go with you."

"It's a smart move on your part to avoid patients."

Wait! This is an entirely new voice! Who is it? It's deep but kind, commanding but gentle, kind of like I always imagined my grandfather's voice would sound. I picture him with a pipe in his mouth.

"The patients here are in serious trouble. You don't want to get mixed up with them."

It's not Satan.

"Who…who are you?"

"I am second in command."

"What do you mean 'second in command'?"

"I represent our Benefactor when he's busy elsewhere."

"Do you mean Satan?

"You will discover in time that He is both my Master and yours."

Has Satan departed? I no longer feel the pressure on my heart.

"Are you a demon, one of Satan's minions?"

I'm afraid of the answer I may get.

"What do you think?" Beth asks. "Should we give it a try?"

"What…?"

"Do you think we should visit the lounge together?"

Not now. Please, not now.

"I'd rather just stay here and read."

"We don't use the word minion," the new voice says gently. "It's demeaning and has a nasty connotation. As I said, I represent our Benevolent Leader."

Oh God, it's one of Satan's minions! He isn't denying it. What am I going to do? My heart sinks in my chest, my breath comes in short gasps. I'm never going to have a moment's peace.

"Why have you suddenly appeared? I gasp.

"Our Master and yours has taken his leave to attend to other business and asked us to work with you while he's gone."

It's just as I feared. God, please help me. But it could be even worse.

"You said 'us.' How many of you are there?"

"Not many are second in command like me. But I have a staggering number of underlings, specialists mostly."

I had no idea this was possible. I'm not sure what to say. I don't want to admit that this terrifies me.

"What should I call you?" I finally stammer.

Not really wanting to know, I feel I have to ask. It might be important to know my enemies by name.

"You can't spend the rest of your life in your room," Beth says. "Don't you even want to take a walk down the hall?"

Please, stop nagging. I can't do it, not now.

"Just call me 'Our Benefactor's First Assistant'."

"But you're a demon."

"We don't use that word either. It's judgmental. Life is too short."

I must call him something other than "Our Benefactor's First Assistant." Satan is not my benefactor.

"I'm going to call you 'One.'"

"If you feel you must."

"Robin . . .," Beth says.

"I don't mind leaving my room," I reply, avoiding eye contact. "I just don't want to spend time with patients."

"I think that's a wise choice," One says. "Patients could contaminate you."

When Mother and I visited Mildred at the State Hospital, I'd been afraid that contact with the patients might contaminate me, making me ill. I'm old enough now to know better, yet a vague but ominous fear remains.

"He's pretty sheltered, isn't he? He's got a lot of catching up to do!"

Suddenly I am nauseated. It's yet another voice.

This voice sounds businesslike, as if its owner doesn't tolerate nonsense well, but it's not as compelling as One's. It sounds more like the voice of a schoolteacher who is determined to keep a rowdy class on topic.

"Who are you?"

"The patients here are nice," Beth says. "You'll like them."

Not now. Not now!

"Although the term is distasteful, we should probably be consistent. You can call me 'Two'."

I don't need to be reminded that they are evil.

"He isn't especially smart, is he?"

It's a third voice! I feel my knees begin to buckle.

This voice is irritating, raspy and aggressive, like a bitter old man.

"Why are you all talking to me?"

"I don't mean to be a nag," Beth continues, "but it would do you good to get out. You've been cooped up in this room for quite a while."

"I was sedated."

"We're here to provide counsel, to help you fulfill your destiny," One says. "You must not be contaminated by others. And you need to be prepared for our Master's return."

"What do you mean by 'contaminated'?"

"No one can be allowed to interfere with your destiny, to distract you," Two replies. "You are to save the many."

As if in response to Two, I feel the presence of my guardian angel again. He's less than a voice and more than an intuition. He provides reassurance.

I shouldn't be listening to demons.

"I don't believe any of you."

"You'll find we're the only ones telling the truth," Two says.

"Dr. Levy thinks it would do you good to get out and talk to the other patients," Beth declares.

I turn to look at Beth, a question on my face.

"Robin, you're not paying attention," Beth gently scolds, stamping her right foot in mock anger. "I'll say it again. It'll do you good to talk to some of the other patients."

"But I'm not sick! And I'm not a patient!"

"We can't recommend mixing with patients," One says. "The risk of contamination is too great. Besides, Dr. Levy and Beth are just trying to get you ready to join your aunt Mildred at Eastern State. I'd be careful if I were you."

"Why would they send me to Eastern State? I'm not crazy, you know."

"Of course you're not crazy," Two agrees. "We're just trying to give you a little warning, that's all. They're not going to tell you the truth until it's too late, until there's nothing you can do to stop them."

"Well, we'll talk about it again later," Beth says. There is determination in her voice. She slowly turns and leaves my room.

Thank God. She's given up, at least for now. I hope Satan will just give up like Beth and leave me alone. But with the appearance of One, Two and Three it doesn't seem likely. What misery will his minions bring down on me?

"Don't worry," Two says. "We're preparing you for your destiny."

This is a destiny I don't want.

"Beth tells me you're not interested in going to the lounge or talking to patients," Dr. Levy says.

"Why is it so important that I spend time with patients?"

Dr. Levy explains that it isn't so important that I spend time with patients, but that I spend time with people. That we need to test the medication I'm taking to make sure it will work when I go home, so I don't have another experience like the one at school and end up right back here in the hospital again.

I admit the medication makes me feel better. The voices don't frighten me as much and it makes me feel safer, that not even Satan is as terrifying when I take it.

He says that if I spend some time in the lounge each day for about a week, and everything goes well, we'll talk about sending me home.

"Don't you ever shut up, Delores?" Henry complains. "You sound like a bloody parrot."

"I should listen to you bitch all day?" Delores snaps.

"Polly wants a cracker. Polly wants a cracker," Henry says. "I can't stand your constant jabbering. A person can't even think."

"Well, it drowns out your God-awful whining."

"Who are these people?" Three asks. "No wonder they're under lock and key!"

Henry and Delores are in continuous motion from the moment I enter the lounge, moving from one chair to another. Their constant bickering makes me wonder if they're married.

"Why are you here?" Two snaps. "You have nothing in common with these halfwits."

Delores finally settles into one of the chairs lining the wall. She's old enough to be my grandmother, but doesn't fit the part. With bleached blond hair and caked-on makeup, she looks hard and bitter. The sickening sweet smell of cheap perfume follows her everywhere.

Uncomfortable, I move back and forth from one end of the couch to the other. I've always been taught that people like Delores are a bad influence. They swear and hang around bowling alleys.

"Don't get involved with these people, Robin," One warns.

"Who's the little brat?" Henry asks, looking first at me and then at Delores.

Henry, who is pacing back and forth, appears to be about as old as my father. His straw-colored hair and complexion, nearly the same, remind me of a cartoon character. He's well over six feet, but far too skinny to scare anyone. Still, it's already clear he can get nasty. I ignore him, hoping he'll leave me alone.

"Don't let Henry worry you. There's nothing he can do to change your destiny," One advises.

"Well, kid, do you have a name?" Henry asks.

Hoping to avoid direct contact with Henry, I turn to Delores.

She simply looks back at me, expecting me to respond.

"My name is Robin."

"There you are, Henry," Delores says. "He's 'Robin Red Breast.'"

"Well I'll be," Henry exclaims. "I thought he was a deaf mute."

"Of course he's not deaf. Are you honey?" Delores remarks, looking first at Henry and then at me. "He just won't talk to the likes of you."

"And I suppose he talks to you because you're some sort of genius. Ha! You don't know from nothing, you bedraggled, old bitch."

"You really know how to charm a lady, don't you? No wonder you've got no family that comes to visit."

Henry looks stung by Delores' comment, but he recovers quickly.

"I wouldn't call your friends from the diner 'family,'" Henry snarls.

"Well, Delores," Henry says, his tone conciliatory. "All I can say is that I don't know why we're here with all these deadbeats." He motions to the other four patients sitting in brown leather chairs that populate the patient lounge.

Why is Henry picking on me? None of the other patients have said a word. They all just sit and stare into space.

"At least we're not boring," Delores responds.

"Sometimes it makes me wonder what it's all about," Henry says. "Why are we stuck in this horrid place? Do you ever think about that, Delores?"

Delores doesn't respond immediately. Finally, with tears forming in the corners of her eyes, she replies.

"I try not to think about it. Life has passed us by, Henry. It's all water over the dam now. I'm more concerned about the kid here. He's so young. What's he doing here? It's a crying shame."

Delores takes out a dainty, heavily perfumed hanky and dries her eyes. Then her face turns hard again.

8

"I don't want it *done*," George declares, as he bursts into the patient lounge.

Of average height and stocky with light brown hair and a bushy mustache, George reminds me of Teddy Roosevelt. He even has a monocle.

"You don't want what done?" Henry asks.

"I don't want shock therapy. Not this week. Not next week. Not ever," George stammers.

George begins to pace rapidly back and forth from the back of the lounge at the French doors to the front near the couch where I'm sitting. Slouched in one of the lounge chairs with his long legs stretched out, Henry jumps up to avoid being trampled by George.

"You're such a baby," Delores observes. "There's nothing to it. It knocks you out. You won't feel a thing."

"I hear that people sometimes break their arms or legs from muscle spasms," Henry says. I could hear the fear in his voice.

With a queasy feeling, I remember the sharp crack when my cousin Larry fell off our backyard swing and broke his arm.

"Well, I've had shock therapy nine times," Delores recounts, "and I've never even broken a fingernail."

"That's because you're a woman," Henry shoots back. "You're weak. Your muscles aren't strong enough to break a bone."

"I'll take you on any day, you wimp," Delores retorts, giving Henry the finger. I could see that her fingernail is perfectly shaped and polished.

"Robin, you need to think about getting out of here," One advises. "These people are just plain wacko."

"Have you ever thought about just leaving?" Two asks.

"Why do you think I keep coming to the lounge? I'm trying to earn my way out of here. And just in case you haven't noticed, the doors are locked."

"You're a smart kid. That shouldn't stop you," Three interjects. "Show a little backbone."

I'm coming to dread Three. He's pushy and his scratchy voice is irritating. He always looks for the worst and then tries to make it even worse than it is. He's the bad cop.

"Yeah, and breaking out will get me into a lot of trouble."

As George sweeps past the coffee table in front of me, the yellow vase of lilac blossoms there suddenly appears brighter than its surroundings. Startled, I lean forward for a closer look. The vase seems to glow as if translucent and lit from within. There appear to be tiny metal shavings floating within the cloud of light that engulfs the vase, shimmering as if magical.

"What is this all about?"

"It's part of your preparation," Two says.

"What preparation?"

"You're being prepared for your destiny."

God help me. Satan and his demons have plans for me. I want no part of it.

Trying to discourage further comment from Three, I focus again on George. He's wearing a faded red robe and brown leather slippers worn down at the heels. His eyepiece keeps popping out as he paces. He is both comical and a little sad.

"You've got to get away from these losers," Three implores. **"Their stupidity might just be contagious. You need to think seriously about busting out of this jail."**

"Look, I'm going home soon. If I bust out now, they'll just lock me up for good."

"Only if they catch you," Two observes.

"I don't have anywhere to go."

"It seems to me that just about anywhere would be better than here," Two suggests. **"Your quack's medication is interfering with your preparation. There's more in store for you than just the yellow vase of lilacs, but you've got to be able to respond to the opportunities that await you."**

My eyes return to the vase. Still looking like it's in a spotlight, it glows a rich yellow. The rest of the lounge now seems to be bathed in subdued light, as if it were dusk.

Am I the only one who can see what's happening? Could this be some weird side effect of my medication?

"They say it wipes out your memory," George complains. "I don't like the sound of that."

What about my weekend in the hospital, the weekend I can't remember? Was I given shock treatments? Wouldn't I have known?

"You raise an interesting question," Two observes. *"You should be told what really did happen to you during the first weekend you were here."*

"Can you tell me?"

"Some things you'll have to discover for yourself," One replies.

Delores catches my eye as she moves from one of the brown leather chairs to another.

"Maybe you'll get lucky and forget how ugly you are," Delores throws back at George.

She laughs at her own joke.

As George passes between me and the coffee table, my eyes are once again drawn to the vase. The color of the vase hasn't changed. Still, the yellow seems richer, deeper, as if it was not just a surface coating, but a color that goes to the core and can't be scraped away.

"Well, you were admitted to the hospital voluntarily, weren't you?" Henry asks.

Henry moves. He likes to sit on the opposite side of the lounge from Delores.

"George is a dunce," Three exclaims. *"Who would voluntarily check into this horror house?"*

The people here are a little weird, but they seem far more ordinary than I had expected, just as Beth suggested. They all seem to be either stressed out or just plain out of it.

"So what if I volunteered?" George replies.

"It means you don't have to do it. You can pack your bags and go home any time you want."

George doesn't respond.

The edges of the vase are now sharply defined, yet the shimmering cloud surrounding it remains. The rest of the lounge is darkening even more, like a movie theater just before the start of the main feature.

"Go ahead, you chicken shit," Delores says. "Just tell them you're scared and want to crawl home to your wife and kids."

"It's not that simple," George mumbles.

"What's not simple?" Henry asks.

"The doctor says I need the shock therapy. And my wife says I can't come home unless I do what the doctor wants."

"This is how it's done here, Robin!" Two declares. "They wear you down, nagging you until you agree to do what they want. Then they've got you."

They'll never wear me down.

"I wouldn't be so smug if I were you," Three replies. "I think you could be in real danger."

"And you do everything your wife says?" Delores queries George. "You are a wimp."

Slowly, the French doors leading from the lounge into the

garden outside begin to glow much like the vase, as if to mark a passage into another world. Convinced the illumination of the vase and French doors, as well as the arrangement of the furniture in the lounge, might be signs from God, I carefully study the layout, the positions of the chairs in relation to the couch and the coffee table, all the spaces and angles in the room.

"I just don't want to forget anything," George murmurs. "I don't want to lose my memory. I don't want to forget who my kids are."

"How are you doing?" Dr. Levy asks as he sits down at the foot of my bed. I had gotten up early and am sitting in my lounge chair. "Are you feeling any better now?"

"Don't tell him about the vase," Two cautions.

"Yes and no."

"Satan to you is still talking, yes?" Sometimes Dr. Levy talks like one of the old Germans in our church, mixing up the normal order of words.

"He only talks to me once in a while. Now it's mostly three of his demons."

I watch closely for Dr. Levy's reaction.

He says nothing but stops to write a long note. He stares at the file for some time and then abruptly looks up straight into my eyes.

"You're rubbing your chest again. It's to keep Satan and his demons out, am I correct?"

I like Dr. Levy's directness. He always says what he means and I don't feel as if he's trying to manipulate me.

I'm beginning, in the presence of Dr. Levy's steady confidence, to feel a little safer.

"Dr. Levy is pathetic," Two interjects. "He's stumbling around like all your relatives. He doesn't know what he's doing. In fact, I think he's a little scary. Who knows what he's going to try next."

"Did you give me shock treatments when I came into the hospital?" I demand to know, a little uneasy with my own directness.

Dr. Levy's eyes widen, revealing his surprise.

"What would make you think that?"

"Shock treatments make you forget."

He looks puzzled.

"Because I can't remember anything about the first weekend I was here."

Dr. Levy nods his understanding.

"Where did you learn about shock treatments?" he asks, his head slightly cocked to one side.

"The patients in the lounge have been talking about it."

"I should have known," he says more to himself than to me. "The answer is no. You haven't received any shock treatments."

I accept Dr. Levy's answer. Alone among the adults I know, Dr. Levy offers me the respect the young usually give, and get, only from each other.

"I'm not sure I'd be so trusting if I were you," One warns.

"Then why can't I remember?"

"Because I gave you a sedative to help you sleep," Dr. Levy replies. "It's as simple as that. You were exhausted and needed rest. You simply slept through the weekend."

"I think you were exhausted because of the medication they gave you," Three interjects. "There's something fishy going on here."

"He just said the sedative was supposed to make me sleep."

"How did you know I was so tired?"

"I think anyone could tell. Satan had been harassing you for about a week, right? That would exhaust anyone."

How does Dr. Levy know so many of the details? I've told him very little. How does he know about my reasons for scraping my chest and my exhaustion?

"How do you know all these things?"

"Well, I suppose it's because I've been at this for a long time."

"He's obviously been talking to your mother," Two says. "Don't give credit he doesn't deserve."

"My mother hasn't figured all this out yet. I'm not so sure that she's been that much help."

"So he's speculating then," Three complains.

"There's more to it than that."

Dr. Levy seems to look right through me for a moment. Maybe he's thinking of other patients.

"Are you going to give me shock treatments?"

I'm afraid of what Dr. Levy's answer might be.

"That's a good question," Two observes. "We can't undo the past for you, but we're here to help you protect yourself from now on. Don't let him worm his way out of answering this question."

"Why do you ask?

"Here he goes again. Pin him down."

"George is getting shock treatments."

"Shock therapy is used for depression and sometimes for uncontrolled mania," Dr. Levy replies calmly. "You're neither depressed nor manic."

My breath escapes. I didn't realize I was holding it.

"Robin, he hasn't said no to the shock treatments," One points out. "Press your question. Don't let him charm you."

"George doesn't want shock therapy. Can they make him do it anyway?"

"Doctors use shock therapy because they think it benefits their patients. Do you think George doesn't want to be helped?"

"I don't know. But I do know the only reason he's agreeing to undergo shock therapy is because his wife is insisting on it. She says he can't come home unless he does what the doctor thinks is best for him. I don't think that's right."

"What don't you think is right?"

"Making someone do something he doesn't want to do."

"It's not at all fair," Two complains. "And it's important for you to be clear about this from the start."

Dr. Levy is quiet for a moment. He gets up from the foot of my bed and begins to pace around the room looking at his feet with his hands clasped behind his back. Then he stops short and looks directly at me.

"Sometimes things just aren't that simple, Robin."

"Oh, boy!" Three exclaims. "He's starting to weave a confusing web of lies. Be careful, Robin."

"What do you mean?"

"I'm not George's doctor, so I don't know the facts. But what if George needs shock treatments?"

"I think George would know."

"Well done," Two says. "Speak up. Set the record straight."

"Sometimes people don't realize they're sick," Dr. Levy continues. "Sometimes they need help from others, but they don't know it."

"How can anyone be sick and not know it?"

"Sometimes a person can know that something has changed within or around him, but doesn't know that it's because of an illness," Dr. Levy replies. "Sometimes our minds can play tricks on us or hide things from us."

"Like a lot of doctors," Two counters, "Dr. Levy is covering his ass. 'I don't know all the facts.' Well, if he doesn't know all the facts, he shouldn't be giving any opinions. Again, he's speculating."

"It's still hard for me to believe that George wouldn't know if he's sick."

"That's it," Three remarks. "Don't back off. Keep him honest."

"Well, you wear glasses," Dr. Levy observes, "but you haven't always worn them, have you?"

"No, but my eyesight has gotten worse."

"So your vision has changed and you got glasses to correct the problem."

"Yes."

"Did you think your eyes had become ill before you got your glasses?" Dr. Levy presses.

"Of course not, my eyesight just changed."

"And life got more difficult for you, didn't it?"

"Well, I couldn't read if that's what you mean."

"So you became less functional, right?"

"What's all this crap about eyesight and functionality?" Three asks. "This is all irrelevant. Be careful, Robin. Your precious doctor is hiding something, something he doesn't want you to know."

"But I wasn't ill."

"But you did need help."

"Yes."

"Maybe George's doctor is just trying to help him, trying

to make life a little easier for George, trying to make him more functional."

"I repeat," Three interjects, "what has this got to with anything?"

"So when did you decide to do something about the condition of your eyes?"

"When Mr. Grimmes got an eye chart and checked everyone's eyesight. Then he told me I needed to get my eyes checked by a doctor, that I probably needed glasses."

"So it did take someone else, someone who intervened to tell you what you needed to know, before you did anything to deal with your problem?"

"I guess that's right."

"What would you say if I told you that George has a medical condition that is making him less functional? Many doctors believe that shock treatments can help with his kind of problem. And what if I told you, that like you when your eyesight first began to deteriorate, George simply doesn't realize what is happening to him, at least not yet. In fact, he may never come to terms with his problems without outside intervention."

"Is that why I'm here? Because I don't know what's good for me? Because I need help but don't know it?"

A look of recognition confirms that Dr. Levy understands the implicit challenge in my question. After circling the room a couple of times, he stops to face me again.

"No, Robin. You're not here because you are unaware of what's good for you. I'm quite convinced you do know what hurts and what heals. You're here because no one else knows what to do with you. No one believes what you've been telling them, that Satan is assaulting you. In fact, you frighten them because they don't understand."

"But I've told them enough about it all that they ought to understand."

"Understanding is important, but it is not the fundamental issue. The real issue is that they don't believe as you do. They simply don't believe Satan and his demons are assaulting you. Or they believe you are possessed."

"Do you know how to help me?"

"You're a bright young man with a lot of potential. Together we will discover what will help you and how to restore your credibility and make others understand."

9

Sitting quietly in the lounge, I wait patiently for the mysterious light to return.

"We told you the yellow vase was only the beginning," Two says.

"I don't know what you're talking about."

"Your preparation, of course," One replies.

"I don't believe in this 'preparation.'"

"Do you deny that yesterday the French doors were illuminated like the yellow vase?" Two asks.

"No. But it has nothing to do with this 'preparation' you're babbling about."

"We're wasting our time with this dingbat!" Three complains. "He just doesn't get it. Even a dunce would know the light clearly indicates the doors lead to somewhere special and the yellow vase marks the way."

What do all these things mean?

"I don't believe they involve any sort of preparation offered by Satan for my benefit, certainly not preparation for some secret destiny. Satan is evil. He deals in darkness not light. He's destructive not constructive, and I know Satan always tries to mislead me."

"These are all lies," One complains.

"If anyone is lying, it's you," I reply.

"Then what could all this possibly mean?" One exclaims in obvious frustration.

Why are my demons trying so hard to convince me it's all part of a blessing from Satan? Why are they so persistent? Why do they even care? Wait a minute! That's it! Satan clearly doesn't work in light. God does!

"These are all signs from God!"

"What?" Three scoffs. "What makes you think something so absurd?"

Satan has no destiny for me and that's why his minions care about the lights. It's because they are messages from God. They fear His intervention. God is communicating with me through these lights. He's cutting through all my demons' chatter and harassments in a way that makes it hard for them to distort His message. That's why Satan stole my prayers. I'm being given a mission from God, and the illuminations are clues to guide me in completing that mission.

This all means that part of my mission is to interpret these signs. My interpretations will tell me how to proceed with my mission in a way that Satan can't corrupt.

"Let me get this straight," Two says. "Our Leader has spent many hours preparing you. He's talked directly to you and offered you wonderful things. He's even sent three of us

to counsel you. Meanwhile, your precious God hasn't even made one appearance. And now you suddenly conclude that the illuminations, our Benefactor's magnificent efforts to prepare you for your destiny, are God's handiwork. That's not only naïve, it's stupid."

"Clearly, God has given me a mission. The only reason Satan and the three of you have been hanging around is to destroy that mission. It's a threat to you."

"Talk about arrogance," Three snarls. **"This is unbelievable."**

"I've been chosen to be God's humble servant."

The lounge door opens with a crash.

"What happened to George?" Delores asks as she saunters in.

She hadn't appeared in the lounge either yesterday or this morning. Without her overpowering perfume, the leather furniture is beginning to smell like a barnyard, burning my nostrils.

George is no longer pacing back and forth, but is withdrawn.

"Well, motor-mouth returns," Henry observes. "You should stay away more often. The silence has been golden."

Henry and Delores are at it again. My heart is thumping like a drum. Although uncomfortable, I watch and listen carefully. Messages from God might come from any source. My altered senses could well reveal secrets concerning the nature of my mission.

"Come on. You're just saying that because you missed me," Delores counters.

"Like a gigantic pain in the ass."

"This Henry is a belligerent one," Two observes. "I'd keep my eye on him."

"Tell me, kid," Delores asks, "What happened to George? The last time I saw him, he couldn't sit still."

"I'm not sure. He's just been sitting around complaining about not wanting shock treatments."

"Let's see if we can get him moving," she urges.

"Leave him alone!" Henry demands. "He's thinking about checking out of this dump."

Delores motions for to me to join her as she approaches George.

"I wouldn't get mixed up in this if I were you," Two says.

Warned by Two and not sure what Delores wants, I stay on the couch.

"Come on, kid. Don't be a stick in the mud. Get yourself over here and help."

Reluctantly, I join her.

"You're making a mistake," Two warns.

She takes George's left arm and motions for me to take his right. Together we pull. Straining, we aren't able to budge him.

"He's like a beached whale," Delores exclaims. "We'll never get him up."

Henry springs up out of his chair and roughly shoves

Delores aside. Losing her hold on George's arm, she stumbles and almost falls.

"We warned you," Two declares.

I make a beeline for my spot back on the couch.

Delores recovers her footing, crosses the room, and carefully sits down, glaring at Henry.

"Are you all right?" Henry asks George.

George doesn't respond.

"That's a fine way to treat a lady," Delores complains bitterly.

"I know how to treat a lady," Henry offers. "There just aren't any in the room."

Delores gives Henry the finger.

Henry just laughs in contempt.

Shaken by what has just occurred, I'm afraid to move. Henry takes on the demeanor of Mr. Grimmes. Expecting him to drag me into the boiler room for a beating, I cower in my corner of the couch.

Henry remains with George.

"Will you ever learn to listen to us?" Three asks. "We're trying to help you. You're lucky you didn't get clobbered."

My heart is beating rapidly. I want to run. Even minor forms of violence upset me. Sports are one thing, but things done in anger or hate always trouble me. My heightened sense of mission makes the evil inherent in such acts even more disturbing.

It surfaces again, the subtle presence of my guardian angel.

I gradually settle down and begin once more to watch for return of the light. When the light finally appears, it falls on George. That another person might be a source of information about my mission, or a doorway to hidden truths, occurs to me for the first time. George is obviously special. I need to find out why.

The nurses on the evening shift usually leave me alone, except to bring my medication, which always includes a sleeping pill.

Under the influence of my nightly sedative, I lie in bed and ponder the day's events. It seems as if I'm dreaming, the real and the imagined mixing freely. The day has taken on extraordinary significance, but the various events are confusing, all parts of the puzzle I'm living. Slipping in and out of sleep, I struggle but I can't make sense of it.

"Concentrate on the portals that you must pass through to complete your preparation," One advises.

The illuminations of the day have all been signs from God concerning my mission. God is communicating directly with me in some sort of code that I must figure out in order to determine the nature of my mission and how best to carry it out. He's using a code that Satan can't decipher.

My demons have deliberately introduced an alternative explanation for the illuminations. They're trying to confuse me. They're introducing evil possibilities into the riddle, making my work far more dangerous.

From what happened to Delores in the lounge today, it's now clear that violence will be involved in my mission, but not necessarily physical violence. Delores has not been physically injured. More than anything, she's been emotionally damaged. But what kind of conflict could possibly be involved in a sacred mission? Maybe the answer is to be found in George.

I slip into an uneasy sleep with the strong sense that the violence has already begun.

Uncle Marvin's sudden appearance in my room startles me. I jerk in surprise, knocking over my carton of milk, dumping the contents onto my breakfast tray.

"Look at you!" Marvin scolds. "You're a mess. Your hair is a rat's nest and you're not even dressed yet."

I say nothing.

"You had better straighten up, young man. You've got your parents spending a fortune on this hospital, not to mention that crackpot doctor. You're acting like a spoiled brat and you are an embarrassment to the whole family."

"Where did this character come from?" Three wonders. "Is he family?"

"He's my uncle."

"Doesn't he know you're being prepared?" Two asks.

"Not that again. Will you please give up?"

"Maybe if you don't say anything, he'll get tired and go away," Three suggests.

"Not Uncle Marvin!"

Marvin, my mother's older brother, worked the farm with his father when the family still lived just outside of Champion, a tiny town in Alberta, Canada. He also assisted his father in digging graves and selling fresh water. He studied late into the night and earned his high school diploma via a correspondence course. He was quite accustomed to long hours of hard labor.

"Dr. Levy's not a crackpot," I reply, poking at my scrambled eggs.

Marvin has little use for psychiatrists. He married Mildred, my father's younger sister. He knew about the Cunningham legacy of mental illness, but he married Mildred all the same. When Mildred got sick and tried to drown their three children, you could see the fear and the pain in his eyes. He didn't sleep for weeks. Mother told me it was because Mildred's psychiatrist insisted that if Marvin's children were ever to see their mother again they would become ill just like her. Mother said the psychiatrist had counseled Marvin to get on with his life for the benefit of the children.

I see that same fear in his eyes now.

"You're not old enough to make that kind of judgment," Marvin declares. "But it's high time you started to act your age. You've got your parents worried sick. If you were mine, I'd straighten you out in no time. And you can bet a good hickory switch would speed things up a bit."

Uncle Marvin is a stickler for discipline. It isn't just the German in him, although his heritage plays a part. Marvin believes discipline is both the secret and the means by which one improves his or her lot in life. When the family moved to Spokane, Marvin took a job in the White Pine Sash Company lumber mill. Over the past 20 years, he'd worked his way up to become president of the corporation.

"Is your whole family like this?" Two asks.

"My mother's family is."

"What about your father and his family?" One inquires.

"My dad's family is not like this, but then he doesn't have much family left."

"What does your dad think?" One continues.

"My dad doesn't think I should be here."

"So let me get this straight," Three exclaimed. "Your father doesn't think you should be here and your mother's whole family thinks it's a waste of time and money. So why are you here?"

"Why don't you ask your Master? He's bound to know the whole story."

"He doesn't tell us everything," One replies. "He seems to think it's better if we have to find out some things for ourselves."

So, Satan is withholding information from his demons. It doesn't sound like Satan is speaking to them in code as God is with me.

"One, I'm here because my mother thinks I need help."

"She's a feisty one, isn't she?" Three observes.

"She's just stubborn."

"Are you listening to me, young man?" Marvin demands. He's close to shouting.

Tongue-tied, not from fear but anger, I'm unable to reply.

"I'm not going to mollycoddle you like your mother does. You'd better be out of here inside a week or you'll pay the piper."

I suddenly realize from the anguish in Marvin's voice, that he isn't angry with me. He's frightened. Although I know I'm not mentally ill, Mildred clearly is, and I suppose Marvin thinks I am too. Not knowing the true nature of my current problem, I can see where Marvin might conclude that his children, my cousins, might follow their mother into insanity. He must think that I'm simply the first of my generation to succumb.

"What's Marvin going to do?" Three asks. "Lynch you on the nearest tree?"

"My uncle can make things hard for me."

"More to the point, does he think he can change things with a lousy hickory switch?"

I decide to ignore Marvin's ranting completely.

"Don't think you can bamboozle me like you have your parents," Marvin warns. "You're going to hear the truth whether you like it or not."

"Just who does he think he is?" One scoffs. "You've got better things to do."

Marvin moves directly in front of me. I stare at his shirt buttons.

"Your childish attempt to get attention isn't going to work," Marvin says. "Your mother and father work hard to put food on the table every day. They don't have time for this."

Satan is attacking me. What makes Marvin think I want attention? I would be much better off if everyone would just leave me alone.

"If it's my parents that put the food on the table," I challenge, "why do we always thank God before every meal?"

I smile broadly. Marvin's face turns beet red.

"You're an ungrateful little brat! How dare you? You'll be . . ."

Glaring at me, Marvin turns and walks out of my room.

My eggs are cold and I'm too upset to finish breakfast. Hoping the light will appear yet again and yield more clues about my mission, I dress and walk down to the patient lounge. When I enter, George is pacing again, the slap of his slippers on the hardwood floor marking the seconds like the rhythmic click of a metronome.

The light is not shining anywhere.

"You might be interested to know that our Leader has decided just today to continue your preparation despite your skepticism," One said.

"Then where is the light that you claim is from him?"

"All in good time," One says "All in good time."

"Well, I've decided!" George exclaims. "I'm not going to do it. I'm checking out of here right after lunch. I don't care what Dora wants."

"Give me a break, George," Delores says. "You'll sit around and whine about the shock treatments until they strap you down and dial up the juice. You don't have the guts to say no."

"Leave him alone," Henry shoots back. "He's made up his mind."

Delores laughs heartily.

"Be quiet, Delores," Henry shouts. "Just ignore her, George. If I were you I'd just focus on getting out of here. You're still the boss."

"If they gave George something to calm him down," Delores said, "it's not working."

"Didn't I tell you to shut up, you old bitch?" Henry replied. "You don't know what you're talking about."

Retreating to my place on the couch, I watch closely as George continues to circle the lounge. I wait.

Nothing happens.

"I think your Leader must have forgotten about me," I say sarcastically.

This could be a good sign.

"Our Master never forgets," Two insists.

Then, as George continues his pacing, my senses explode. The strong smell of his sweat arrives before he does, making me gag. As he passes, waves of heat roll off him and over me like a hot desert wind. He's leaving a charge of static electricity in his wake that makes the hair on my arms stand on end. George is transmitting his distress in wave after wave of nervous energy that rises and falls like the wail of a siren.

"Why don't you sit down and relax, George?" Delores says softly. "You're going to wear yourself out, not to mention the rest of us."

George's pain is contagious. His agonies pound on me like fists. The steady thumping of his slippers drives these sensations into me with the force of a jackhammer.

"For crying out loud, just leave him alone," Henry demands.

I barely hear Henry's response to Delores.

George is confused. He's afraid he'll lose his memory, which is the same as losing time. Time not remembered is time lost. With shock treatments, George would be expected to lose both memory and time, neither of which he'll ever get back. The doctors are going to take these from him against his will. It's worse than theft. It is an act of considerable violence. No wonder he's in agony.

"I'm only trying to help," Delores replies. "He's got himself all worked up."

The connection between George and me is becoming clearer, but there's still a lot I don't understand. If the doctors' shock treatments rob George of time and some of his memory, where do these go? I've already lost both time and memory, but for me it's because of sedatives, not shock treatments. George and I may be expected to experience similar forms of violence. His pain is my pain. In a sense, we're connected, but how closely? God is clearly trying to tell me I have important connections with all of humanity. He's also trying to inform me that an understanding of time, the passage of time, or perhaps the loss of time, is somehow essential to my mission. But why is it essential? Deciphering God's clues is not easy.

Time may stop for George because of shock treatments, but will it also stop for me? Is our connection that complete? Will I even recognize it if time stops for me? I didn't recognize that time had stopped for me because of the sedatives. A nurse had to tell me. And again, where do time and memories go when we lose them? Is my mind supposed to serve as some sort of temporary storage place for George's memories? Will I even be aware of it if this occurs? Or will it be a subconscious event? Is George supposed to do the same for me?

Is all this about humans maintaining their connections? Is there some collective unconsciousness like a bank where all these lost memories and lost time can be deposited for later use? Can they be retrieved or reused? Will all of mankind cease to exist if this common unconsciousness fails, even for a single moment? The possibilities are both exciting and terrifying.

"I don't think your Master is going to make an appearance."

"Our Benefactor," One replies, "is waiting for you to accept his offer and time is of the essence. You must do this soon. He's been very patient with you."

"George has been sitting around for days like the rest of these zombies," Delores observes, motioning to the three other patients now sitting silently staring into space. "This sudden burst of pacing around is going to give him a heart attack."

"Since when does a lousy waitress from a cheap diner know anything about medicine?" Henry scoffs.

Is George a master of all time? Can he control it, making it go forward or backward at will? Is that why I am connected to him? As part of my mission from God, am I supposed to take over the management of time from George? Is there a transfer of power in the making? Am I supposed to save all of humanity through the manipulation of time? Is God asking me to somehow postpone the judgment day?

Again, the rhythmic slapping of George's slippers seems to say it is so.

George continues to pace around the room oblivious of everything around him. Then, suddenly, he stops short and turns to look at me as the light descends on him.

Can a person possibly be a clue from God? Is God going to enable me to control the passage of time? Is this somehow part of my mission?

I stare at George in awe. He stares back as if to confirm my suspicions.

My demons are still trying to confuse me. Is this just another attempt by Satan to lead me astray? The difference and the consequences are profound. Satan is trying to infiltrate my mission with this preparation nonsense of his, to confuse and destroy me. But I know the truth! God is finally answering all Satan's blasphemous claims.

I decide to put it to a test.

If I am to control the passage of time, it is essential that I strengthen my abilities. George represents a potential opportunity to do this. I need to carefully manage my relationship with him. George and I seem to be communicating by thought alone. If I can control George in this fashion, it will give me a window into controlling time itself. And if I can control George, I'll probably be able to control others as well.

"You will save the many," One exclaims, parroting Satan's thought insertions.

"Not that again. What do you mean by 'I will save the many'?"

No one responds.

"Well, anyone can see George is so wound up, he's going to self-destruct," Delores says.

"What do you mean?" I repeat.

"It will be revealed."

Satan hasn't told them what my "destiny" is to be! My demons are operating in the dark!

Determined to find out if George and I can communicate

by thought, I decide to see if he will accept simple instructions from me. Looking at George, I silently send him a command to stop pacing and sit down.

George maintains his cadence.

I try again. George fails to respond.

I have to know. It will confirm that all the signs I've been seeing are, in fact, from God.

Clearing my mind and holding my breath, I focus all my thoughts on George, commanding him to sit down.

Nothing!

What if I'm wrong? Are the mysterious light and the passage of time of no significance? Is it possible that God has not given me a mission? Have I imagined all this? Panic turns my stomach over, leaving me nauseated. I jump up from the couch to head for the restroom.

"Finally," Delores says as George sits down. "That's it, George. Relax like a good boy."

I stop dead in my tracks.

10

When I enter the lounge two days later, I find George sitting quietly in one of the lounge chairs. Staring straight ahead, he appears to see nothing. It's almost as if he isn't quite there.

Henry enters the lounge just behind me.

"Why is George here?" Henry asks. "I thought he checked out."

"I told you so," Delores says, a note of satisfaction in her voice. "George had his first shock treatment yesterday."

"What?" Henry exclaims.

"I told you he'd chicken out," Delores says. "Too bad you weren't here yesterday, you wise ass. He was whining right up to the minute they came and got him."

"You bitch," Henry shouts. "It's all your fault. Why can't you just keep your mouth shut?"

Henry walks over to where George is sitting in silence and looks directly into his eyes.

"We told you," Two says. *"They wear you down until you do what they want, just like George. You need to get out of here NOW."*

"But you know I can stop them from doing anything to me."

"I wouldn't be so sure. What if they knock you out first?"

"It doesn't matter anyway. Dr. Levy says I'm not going to get shock treatments."

"Amazing," Three says. *"I don't understand why he continues to believe everything his quack tells him."*

"Give him a little time," One responds.

"He's running out of time," Three replies. *"Our Leader has been more than patient."*

"You always expect the worst. If I listened to everything you say, I'd be in a panic all the time. Since I've taken over control of the flow of time from George, your 'destiny' no longer concerns me."

"Where did this crazy idea come from?" Three interjects, his voice wavering. *"Is he going over the hill after all the time we've spent on him?"*

George remains unresponsive. I have to look closely to see that he's breathing. It appears as if nothing could wake him from his trance. But, George and I have a secret. I know what has really happened. I've simply moved George and all the rest of us forward past the time of his shock treatment. Although everyone thinks otherwise, his shock treatment never occurred. He hasn't forgotten anything. He's just confused. His ordeal is over. It's now time for me to bring him back to life, to place him in the here and now.

I focus my thoughts, telling George to say something.

I wait.

Nothing!

Concentrating hard, I silently order George to stand up.

He remains hunched over, showing no signs of life except for a slight rise and fall of his chest.

I command George to get up and walk.

He doesn't budge.

This doesn't bother me. I'm certain the power is still within me. I feel it flowing through my body and extending out to touch George.

So why isn't he responding? Are Satan and his demons interfering?

Delores moves closer to George and stares into his eyes. Henry, watching Delores intently, also moves in closer.

"He's not a vegetable," she observes. "He'll be a lot better in a day or two and back to himself in a week. The effects of the shock treatment won't last that long. Then he can go home to the wife and kids. May God have mercy on them all."

I smile. I've fooled them all.

Delores' face clouds over and she speaks softly, wistfully.

"But I can tell you right now that he'll be back, just like the rest of us. You can never escape, you know."

"See," Two says, "she's confirmed what we've been saying. Once they get you started, they've got you forever."

Even my demons don't know what I have done.

"Now's the time to get out." Three adds. "It may be your last chance."

"You can't fool me with this scare tactic anymore. I can control the passage of time. Last chances are no longer a concern of mine."

"What time is it?" George mumbles.

I knew it! My commands work!

"Well, what do you know," Delores says. "The Fearless Crusader speaks. Will wonders never cease?"

"Can't you keep your mouth shut, even for just a little while?" Henry snaps.

"Trust me, you idiot," Delores fires back. "He doesn't know what he's doing. Now that he's talking, he'll be asking a lot of questions. Most of them won't make any sense."

Henry moved to sit down next to George.

"What did you say, George?" Henry asks.

George doesn't respond immediately.

"What time is it?"

"It's about one o'clock," Henry replies.

"When do you think they'll come for me?"

"Come for you?"

"For my shock treatment. It's scheduled for this afternoon."

"You've already had your shock treatment."

"No. I've been waiting for them to come. I'm going to tell them I won't do it."

Without warning, George stands up.

"You can't remember your shock treatment, your highness," Delores breaks in. "They fried your brain two days ago."

Concern appears on George's face, eventually dissolving into an uncertain frown.

"Who did they fry?" he stammers.

Henry turns and glares at Delores.

"They fried…"

"Shut up, bitch," Henry shouts.

George stumbles forward, narrowly avoiding a fall as he bumps into the coffee table. Henry leads him back to his chair.

That's enough proof for me. I clearly still have the power!

"When are they going to do you, Hon?" Delores asks, looking at me.

"You mean give me a shock treatment?" I ask.

"Yes, Honey. You'll get the treatment, just like the rest of the mummies around here."

"Oh, I'm not getting shock treatments."

Henry turns. Both he and Delores are now staring at me.

"Then why on earth are you here?" Henry asks.

"There must be a reason," Delores probes. "Aren't you depressed, I mean, aren't you tired all the time, or don't you feel down in the dumps? You don't talk much, you know."

"No, Dr. Levy told me I'm not depressed. I'm not going to get shock treatments."

"Then why are you here?" Delores asks again, looking puzzled.

"Because Satan's putting thoughts into my mind and his demons are talking to me."

The room goes silent.

"You shouldn't have told them about us," Two says. "It always causes problems."

My skin tightens and my heart beats faster.

After what seems like several minutes, Henry speaks.

"Lord, help us! We've got ourselves an honest to God crazy person here. He's the real McCoy."

Henry moves away from me.

My heart is beating so hard I can hear the pounding in my ears.

"Don't pay any attention to him, Honey. He doesn't know what he's talking about."

"Get him out of here," Henry declares, sounding like the leader of an angry lynch mob.

"What in the world are you talking about?" Delores asks.

"You can never tell what a crazy person is going to do. He

could slit our throats in our sleep. I'm talking to my doctor. Schizos belong out at the State Hospital with the rest of the crazies."

"Be quiet, Henry," Delores commands. "He doesn't talk like one of those schizos. I mean you can understand what he says."

Delores turns to me.

"Don't pay any attention to him, Hon."

Henry laughs.

"You're going out to Eastern State," Henry says, "and once you get there, they'll never let you out. There's nothing that will cure a schizo."

"I'm going home soon," I say. "Dr. Levy promised."

"I understand Henry yelled at you yesterday," Dr. Levy says, sitting at the foot of my bed.

His glasses slide down his nose. He doesn't seem to notice.

"He called me a 'schizo.'"

"Beth says you handled it pretty well. I'm proud of you. That tells me your medication is working. What do you think?"

"Well, Henry scared me a little when he started shouting. But he can call me anything he wants. It doesn't mean a thing because he doesn't know what he's talking about."

"It wasn't like at school with Mr. Grimmes, was it?"

"No, not at all. I'm fine. It was just the shouting. Henry's pretty big and he was upset."

"People may call you names when you go home, you know."

"My family would never call me names."

"The kids at school might. Do you think that will bother you?"

"No. I'll just ignore them."

"Well, Robin, I've got good news. I've talked to your parents and I'm sending you home on Friday."

"Can I play softball with my church team and go to summer camp?"

"Softball is fine. We'll have to see how you do before we decide about summer camp."

"Thanks, Dr. Levy."

"Like I said, I'm proud of you. You've done most of the work. You're a fine young man."

Dr. Levy gets up to go.

"Dr. Levy?"

'Yes?"

"What's a 'schizo'?"

"It's an unkind word that usually refers to someone with schizophrenia."

"What's schizophrenia?"

"Schizophrenia is a condition of the brain."

"If you get schizophrenia, what happens to your brain?"

"We think the chemistry in your brain changes. The brain is a complex organ, so we're not yet sure precisely what happens and we're not sure what causes schizophrenia."

Chemistry? Like the chemistry I do with my chemistry set? That's a strange idea!

"You mean my brain has chemistry?" I asked. My surprise was obvious.

"We've recently developed a medication that seems to help. You're taking that medication now."

I've never thought of a medication as a chemical.

"Does it affect your sugar levels like diabetes? My aunt Mildred has diabetes and takes insulin."

"No, it affects what patients believe, and how they think and behave."

"Like, how?"

Dr. Levy thinks for a minute.

"Well, for example, sometimes patients with schizophrenia think that ordinary things have special meanings that only they can decipher."

"Oh."

I'm glad I haven't told Dr. Levy about the mysterious light.

Dr. Levy turns to go.

"Doctor."

"Yes?"

"You should know that I'll be just fine at home. What other people say or do won't bother me because I can control their thoughts and their behavior if I have to."

"Don't be an idiot," Three says. "The more you tell this quack about these crazy ideas of yours, the more likely you are to end up in Eastern State."

"And if things get truly bad, I can control time, make it stop or go backwards, like I did with George. I stopped time for him so he wouldn't get shock therapy. Everyone else thinks he had a shock treatment and just can't remember it, but George and I know he never had one."

Dr. Levy looks at me as if I'm an old acquaintance, almost as if we'd had this conversation before.

11

I burst through the hospital exit doors into the sunlight, thrilled to be free at last. Filled with joy, I feel as if I could fly, just like my namesake. I see Mother's car parked on the street to my left, turn and dash towards it with abandon. The toe of my right shoe catches in a crack between slabs of sidewalk and I do leave the ground for a moment. While I am airborne, my newly found freedom seems to support me, to hold up my body and my spirit. Then I go down hard, pitching forward in a belly flop onto the concrete sidewalk.

Mother drops my bag and runs to catch up.

"Robin, are you okay?" she asks, kneeling at my side.

The palms of my hands are scraped and the left leg of my corduroy pants is torn. My knee is cut. Warm blood trickles from my nose, dripping off my chin.

"I'm all right," I say.

Pulling a handkerchief from my back pocket, I pinch my nose.

"But you're all skinned up."

"I'll be just fine," I say, with a nasal twang. "Let's just go home."

"You should be more careful."

"I just want to go, to leave this place."

"Well, pick yourself up. We'll go clean up your knee and bandage it."

As I start to get up I realize I'm not "just fine." Some of my special powers have drained away, leaving a void. Suddenly I feel sick and dizzy, as if I were bleeding profusely. I'm afraid I will pass out. The loss of these powers, which had sustained me in recent days, leaves me weak and nauseated. I sink back onto the pavement, my bloody hand to my mouth.

How did this happen? What does it mean? Is my mission already in danger? What should I do?

Suddenly freezing cold, I realize that Satan is trying to fill the empty space with evil. I begin to shake all over from the chill.

I must combat this evil within me, to fight off Satan and his demons. I can't afford to lose any of my powers or allow them to be diluted. I shouldn't –

Mother takes me by the shoulders and shakes me.

"Robin. What are you doing?"

I must resist any distractions. I have to think. What is it I shouldn't do?

"Relax," Two commands. "You're imagining things."

I shouldn't step on cracks. That's it! My powers are being drained away by my demons when I step on cracks. I must concentrate. I must figure all this out.

"He certainly has a vivid imagination," Two says.

"Robin, you're acting like an idiot," Three adds. *"You don't have special powers. We're here simply to advise you. We're on your side. Get a grip."*

I must not listen to them. I need to protect my powers, my mission. I can't allow myself to be misled by their lies or distracted by any –

Mother shakes me again.

"Robin! Get a hold of yourself. We have to go."

"What?"

"Get up. We have to go."

She doesn't understand. Why doesn't she understand? She knows about Satan and his demons. She's warned me about them for years. They all have—Mr. Grimmes, Pastor Voelcker, my Sunday School teachers. Even our daily devotions at home often contain warnings.

Mother grabs my arm and pulls me up off the pavement.

"I've got to stop by the store. We'll get a bottle of iodine to disinfect your knee."

Drained of energy, my knees almost buckle.

"I thought we're going home."

"I'm sorry you have to endure this," One remarks. *"But you must know by now that the store is more important to your parents than you are."*

One's comment cuts like a knife, slicing a nerve already laid bare by the constant harassment of the demons. As always, I struggle in vain to ignore the searing pain of being less important than my parents' store.

"The delivery men expect to be paid tomorrow," Mother continues. "It'll only take a few minutes to sign their checks."

I resent her petty concern with the store.

"It's okay," I mumble, slumping in the passenger's seat of my mother's '46 Dodge.

Removing the handkerchief from my nose, I find the bleeding has stopped.

"I hope your scuffed hand and knee heal quickly. Your first softball game is on Wednesday. Coach says he needs you on second base. He doesn't have anyone who's right for the position."

Uncle Ray coaches our church's softball teams, but family members are always careful to call him "Coach" during the season. He's determined not to favor kin.

Playing second is important to me. For five years, I'd played the position on our church's junior league team. Now I get to play on the men's team. It's a big challenge.

"Good," Three says. "Play ball. Forget this delusion of yours about a mission from God. In fact, just forget about God. He's forgotten about you."

"God hasn't forgotten about me. I won't let you steal my powers."

"What kind of a God sends someone, anyone, to the hospital you've just escaped?" Two continues. "Your enhanced perceptions are a gift from our Master. He's got wonderful plans for you."

"You can't fool me that easily. Do you think I'm stupid?"

116

***"He'll never catch on,"* Three snarls.**

"Robin? Do you hear me?

"What?"

"Coach has called a special practice for Monday night. You need to get ready."

Attempting to ignore my demons, I try to focus on what my mother's saying.

"Do you think Dad can hit some grounders for me to field this weekend? It'd be good practice."

"You know your father works Saturday and Sunday."

"Yeah, but…"

"Your brother's coming home for the summer sometime on Sunday. If it's not too late and he's not too tired, he might hit some grounders for you."

"That'd be okay."

But I know that everyone will want to catch up with the latest news when Carl gets home and we'll never get to softball.

"It'll be wonderful to have you home again, especially with your brother here for the summer. Robin, I'm so proud of you." Mother reaches across the front seat to tousle my hair. "Things are finally getting back to normal."

Entering the store behind Mother, I know right away I'm in serious trouble. I had just lost some of my special powers by stepping on a crack in the sidewalk. I'm still weak and a little nauseated from that experience. I'm afraid of what will happen to me if lose any more of my special powers. And now, spread out before me is a floor covered with linoleum tile. The joints form a huge grid of cracks. As Mother walks briskly toward the rear of the store, I soon fall behind, tiptoeing from one tile to the next, trying to avoid these cracks, trying desperately to prevent any further loss of my powers.

Once Mother has passed, the clerks in the checkouts watch me out of the corners of their eyes, pretending they haven't noticed. Customers turn to stare at me openly, whispering among themselves.

"What's he doing, Mommy?" a little girl asks. "Is he playing hopscotch?"

"Never mind, Sally," her mother replies.

An eerie silence falls over the area.

They're all passing judgment on me, on what I'm doing. They don't understand. I have no choice. I can't let them get in the way. I must protect myself from a loss of powers and the ignorance of those around me.

I pretend I didn't hear what the little girl said.

Trying to cover two tiles with each step to avoid taking baby steps, I soon discover that my legs won't reach. I step on a crack. Power immediately begins to drain from me. Again, I feel as if I'm bleeding. Stopping abruptly, I snatch my foot back, careful to plant it squarely in the middle of a tile. Baby steps provide my only passage, as if I were picking my way across a swollen creek in spring by stepping from one protruding stone to the next. The tiles feel uneven and slippery, as if I might simply slide off and into the net of cracks.

"You're making a fool of yourself," Three says mockingly.

118

"Thanks for the encouragement."

"Who cares what the little girl thinks?" Two interjects.

"I don't. I wish they would all just go away."

"Then join us. Our Leader has wonderful plans for you. He has much to show you."

"You're trying to mislead me…"

"Wise up, you stupid fool," Three exclaims. "You have no special…"

"Silence," One commands. "Give him a chance to figure it all out."

"You're not my friends. You harass me."

"No matter how hard we try or what we do to educate him," Three retorts, "he doesn't get it."

"What's he doing now, Mommy? Why's he just standing there looking at the floor?"

The little girl's voice comes from far away.

It seems like only a moment has passed, but when I look up, Mother is most of the way down the main aisle. When she turns and sees me taking baby steps, the broad smile on her face changes first into a look of astonishment, then embarrassment. She rushes back and grabs my arm. Dragging me toward the backroom of the store, she doesn't stop until we're out of view of customers and employees. A substantial amount of my powers drain away as she pulls me along and I unwillingly step on cracks.

Why is my mother doing this? Doesn't she care what happens to me? Doesn't she know that this drains away my powers and threatens to fill the void with evil?

"What was all that about?" Mother demands. "I thought you were all over that sort of nonsense."

I'm angry but know better than to complain.

"This new thing you're doing, this tiptoeing is worse than when you went into the hospital!"

Mother is holding back tears. She sits down at her desk and takes the company checkbook out of the center drawer.

I shrink into the chair at the side of her desk.

"Robin, you're out of the hospital now. You can't behave this way. You don't want me to take you right back, do you?"

Her threat increases my anxiety.

I haven't even gotten home yet. Would she really take me back?

"Well?"

"No. I don't want to go back."

"Then you'll have to stop this sort of thing."

"But I can't step on cracks!"

"Nonsense! Don't force me to talk to Dr. Levy about this."

She doesn't understand. No one in my family understands. They all seem to think I'm spoiled, acting out, or sick. They all assume I can simply change everything if I want to.

"What do you expect?" Three sneers. "They're all simpletons. They have no appreciation of your destiny and the nature of the preparation in which you are engaged."

"I will not engage in any sort of 'preparation' or anything else you propose."

Everyone has warned me all my life that Satan is after me. Why can't they see what's happening to me?

"First of all, our Master is not 'after you.' He's offering you a splendid opportunity. Show a little respect, a little gratitude. Besides, none of your elders believe all the things they've taught you over the years," Two explains. "They're a pack of hypocrites."

"You're wrong."

"Actions speak louder than words."

"Good," Mother says. "Then it's settled."

Does she really think I'll abandon God's plan for me? Are my demons right? How can she believe all the things she's taught me and then treat me this way?

"When's he going to figure out that parents use the threat of God's anger to control their kids?" Three remarks.

Again I try but can't block out Three's comment.

"Where's Dad?" I blurt out, startling Mother.

"It's Friday afternoon. He's in the conference room talking to salesmen."

"Doesn't he know I'm coming home?"

"Yes, he knows."

"Should I tell him I'm here?"

"Robin, you know we never interrupt when your father is

talking to salesmen."

"But I just thought…"

"No buts. Your father's busy."

Father's always working. He never found time to visit me in the hospital. I must be foolish to think he'd interrupt his stupid meeting. And I know I won't see him this weekend. He'll be working just like every other weekend.

I stare down at my shoes.

"But can't I just say hello?"

"Robin, you know better."

"You know your father never did give a hoot about you," **Three interrupts.**

Three's comment hurts more than most because I fear it might be true.

"That's not true," I plead.

"Don't exaggerate, Three," Two says. "He cares about Robin, but sadly, he thinks the store is more important."

"That's not true either!"

"Unfortunately, Robin, you've got to face the facts," One insists.

"Oh yeah! And what are those?"

"Just stop and think for a moment about your uncle Ray and aunt Ester," One says.

Ester is my mother's younger sister. She's a natural blond,

tall like my father, and quite attractive. My father asked her out a few times, until he met my mother. I'm told it was love at first sight. Uncle Ray had a thing about my mother, but lost out to my father. Ray and Ester were married a year or so after my parents.

My grandfather owned a small grocery store, which he left to Ester when he died. Ray trained as a butcher and was not much interested in the rest of the business, which Ester ran. When it became too much for the two of them, they invited my parents to join them as equal partners. My mother had worked in the store from the age of 16 until she married my father. Ray and Ester ran the meat department and my father ran most everything else. My mother did the bookkeeping.

"What about Ray and Ester?"

"As equal partners their interest in the success of the store should be the same as your mother's and father's, right?"

"What's your point?"

"Who takes you fishing? Hunting? Camping? Who coaches the softball team?"

"Uncle Ray. So?"

"Why doesn't your father do these things?"

"He's busy at the store."

"If the store requires so much work, how do Ray and Ester find time to do things with you, but not your father?"

A hard knot forms in my gut.

"We can only conclude that your father spends his time at the store, while Ray and Ester take you fishing, because your father cares more about the store than he does about you," **Two reasons.**

"My father buys me great things for Christmas and my birthday," I insist.

"Like the red wagon with the whitewall tires?" Three asks.

This comment stings.

"How do you know about my red wagon?"

"We're supposed to help you," Two counters. "We've been briefed about the red wagon. Your father gave it to you for your birthday and then took it a week later to use at the store. You never got it back. Am I right?"

What else do they know? Is nothing hidden from them?

"Even your Uncle Marvin takes you camping."

My stomach churns.

"And when your father does take time off from the store, he doesn't spend it with you," Three adds. "He works at the church. Has he ever asked you to help him?"

I'm afraid I'm going to throw up.

"Robin, are you okay?" Mother asks. "You look sick."

"What?"

"You're not paying attention. Did you hear what I just said?"

I have no idea.

"Well?"

"I didn't hear you."

"Honestly, Robin," Mother says. "If I didn't see you sitting here, I'd think you were somewhere else. Try to pay attention."

It's Saturday morning. My medication is still making me tired and I wake up around 10 a.m. to find the house empty.

"We haven't had an entire day to ourselves in a long time," One says.

My heart aches. I haven't yet had a chance to talk to my father. Last night he fell asleep in his chair right after he got home from work. I feel empty and alone.

"Last night your mother kept talking about the good old times, about things getting back to normal," Two says.

"So my mother is guilty of wishful thinking, too."

"Well, she's dreaming. Things will never be the same again. Our Master has endowed you with a destiny that will make the 'good old days' pale by comparison."

"I don't think the 'good old days' were all that good. I want things to change, to get better."

"But things have changed. They are better and you have our Leader to thank."

"I thank your Leader for nothing. He's a curse. He's only made things worse, much worse."

"We still have today," One says.

"What's so good about today?"

"We can talk about this in peace. Our conversations get so confusing when we're constantly being interrupted by others.

It'll be nice to just have a chance for some straight talk again."

"You never talk straight. You're always lying to me, trying to lead me astray, trying to mess me up."

"We've never lied to you," Two retorts. "You just haven't seen the whole truth yet."

I sense the presence of my guardian angel again. He's listening in on this conversation with great interest.

"Look. I don't want to talk to you guys anymore. This is a good time for you all to leave. Go back to wherever you came from."

"We can't do that," Two counters. "We have a charge from our Benefactor to educate you, to teach you the truth. We can't abandon our responsibilities."

I try to ignore my demons for the rest of the day, but it's impossible. They continue to harass me. Without the interference of anyone else, without the chaos of conflicting demands on my attention, there is nothing to offset their constant badgering. Their voices seem louder and more insistent. By the end of the day my nerves are shot. My demons have completely worn me out.

12

We are having the usual Sunday morning breakfast of white toast, fried eggs, bacon, orange juice and milk. I'm dressed in my suit and tie.

"Robin, you forgot to comb your hair," Mother reminds me, "and your tie's crooked. What's gotten into you? You're always so neat."

"Your mother's turned into a real nag," Three claims. "She's always carping about how you look, like it's a big deal."

"I'm way too busy dealing with you to worry about whether I look like a perfect gentleman."

Except for Mother's complaints, it feels good to get back into our family routine. Everything's proceeding as always on Sunday mornings until we turn left instead of right out of our driveway.

"Aren't we going to church?" I ask.

"We are," Father replies, "but we're going to a different church now."

"A new church? What about Redeemer? We always go to Redeemer."

"We left Redeemer," Mother replied. "We started at Holy Cross while you were in the hospital."

"What about my friends? When will I see them?"

What'll I do without my friends?

"Your folks don't care about your friends," Three points out.

"You'll make new friends," Mother says gently, trying to console me. "It'll give you a chance to start over now that you're out of the hospital."

New friends! Does she have any idea how hard it is to make new friends?

"I don't want new friends."

"You'll be just fine."

But I won't be just fine. My difficulty in forming close friendships has always resulted in a certain loneliness and self-doubt. I want to be accepted, but always feel like I'm somehow different.

"And just why are we changing churches?" I demand, pushing on the back of the front seat with my feet. My mouth is dry.

"You embarrassed your mother at Redeemer," Two sneers. "She's ashamed of you."

"My mother isn't ashamed of me."

"Your behavior has become rather bizarre, you know."

"I don't like your tone of voice, young man," Mother replies, turning to glare at me, the smell of Clorets mints on her breath.

"I'm sorry," I say, crossing my fingers behind my back.

I speak more respectfully, hiding my anger. I want to know the real reason.

"Why are we going to Holy Cross?"

No one asked me about what I'd like.

"Wise up," Three says. "They don't care about your feelings."

"Reverend Voelcker left Redeemer while you were in the hospital," Father explains. "The new minister and I don't see eye to eye."

"Why not?"

"He's closing the school."

"Do you mean Redeemer Lutheran? That's my school!"

"Remember, Robin, it's not your school anymore. You graduated," Mother said.

"Then why do we care?"

"Robin!" Mother reprimands me. "You should be ashamed of yourself. What about all the other children that are still attending the school?"

"I told you she's ashamed of you," Three snickers.

Did Reverend Voelcker leave because of me?

"Why did Reverend Voelcker leave?" I ask.

"It's nothing you need to be concerned about," Father says, his voice soft as always.

"But I'll never see my friends again."

"The kids at Holy Cross are nice," Mother responds. "You'll make new friends. Now that you've graduated from grade school, you can join the youth group at Holy Cross. They have a lot of great activities. You'll love it."

I don't care about activities.

When we get to Holy Cross, I refuse to get out of the car. Mother is furious. But, in frustration, she finally leaves me there.

Mother won't forget this. It's certain to come back to haunt me, but I don't care. She can do what she wants to punish me for defying her. Why didn't my parents ask me if I'm willing to leave Redeemer, to give up my friends?

"Okay, Robin, all we need is a simple base hit," Coach says as he hands me my favorite bat. It is six weeks since we left Redeemer and four weeks into the summer softball season. We are playing Redeemer for the first time.

Uncle Ray and his family promptly followed us to Holy Cross. Being the best in the league, "Coach" is soon leading the Holy Cross softball team.

It's ironic that the first game I play on the Holy Cross team is against Redeemer. I know more about the men on the opposing team than my new teammates.

"Come on, Rob, just a hit, nothing fancy."

Others from the Holy Cross bench join in the chatter.

My heartbeat quickens and my chest swells with pride at my new team's faith in me. This isn't junior league anymore.

Stopping short of the batter's box, I scoop up a little of the fine powdery baseline dirt, rubbing it on my hands and the grip of my bat. Tapping the inside of both shoes, I knock off the clumps of dirt and grass that are stuck to my cleats.

"Who do you think you are," Three jeers, "Babe Ruth?"

Stepping into the batter's box, I stand erect to plant my feet and then crouch slightly, my bat cocked up high behind me. I try to look confident, but Spencer Hamlin is pitching for Redeemer and I know he's good.

"You're dead meat. Spencer's seen you play. He knows you're a sucker for a slow ball," Three jeers.

With Erik on second base and someone I don't know on third, a simple base hit will give us a couple of runs.

"Take your time," someone calls out. "Take your time. We only need a single."

I don't know many of the names of my teammates or our supporters yet.

The first pitch is a curve ball that drifts high and wide. The catcher breaks his stance to snag it. I let it pass without flinching.

"Ball one," the umpire calls out in a clear voice that carries over the field and into the grandstands.

"Spencer's setting you up," Three warns.

"That a boy," a teammate calls from the bench. "Wait for one right down the pipe. There's no rush."

Other teammates shout words of encouragement.

"You've got one on him now. Just let him think about it."

Tapping the plate with the end of my bat, I raise a small cloud of dust. The umpire waves the catcher aside and sweeps the plate.

"Scared are you?" Three asks. "Are you stalling for time?"

The second pitch comes with blistering speed, but is inside and high.

By jerking my head back and dropping back out of the batter's box, I avoid being hit.

Is Spencer trying to frighten me? Is he angry that I left the Redeemer team, his team?

"Ball two," the umpire's voice rings out.

The chatter from my teammates continues uninterrupted.

"You've got him on the run now," a Holy Cross supporter hollers. "He's throwing bean balls."

"He knows a good hitter when he sees one," another fan shouts.

"The pitcher's going wild," a woman yells. "He's losing it."

"Wait him out," yet another rooter shoots. "Wait him out."

The fielders on the other team respond with words of encouragement for Spencer.

"This guy's just off the junior league team, Spence. It's the crazy Cunningham kid. You can take him out easy."

The crazy Cunningham kid! Is this what all the Redeemer players think?

The wives, girlfriends, and daughters of my new team members increase their chatter. They are rooting for me. It feels good to be on the men's team at last.

Maybe I can make some new friends at Holy Cross.

"Hit a homer. Knock it out of the park. Hit a homer. Knock it out of the park."

The presence of female voices is new to me. I feel more the man for it. My confidence soars. I would love to drive in two runs.

"Do you see Janice in the stands on the other side?" *Three asks.*

"Of course I do. So what?"

"I think she's sweet on you."

"Leave me alone. I'm playing softball."

"But she… "

Spencer delivers another fastball. Luckily, it bounces in front of the plate. I didn't even see it coming.

"Ball three."

"You guys made me miss that pitch completely. You've got to leave me alone. I'm trying to play softball."

"But we have weighty matters to discuss with you," *One* insists. ***"You can't just expect us to disappear."***

"Janice is not a weighty matter."

"You're right about that," *Three agrees.* ***"She's got a great figure."***

"Be quiet," One says. "We do have important things to discuss, like our Benefactor's plans for Robin."

"My gifts are from God. How many times..."

"You got him in a 3 and 0 count," one of my teammates calls out. "Wait the pitcher out. Just let the next pitch go. He's going to walk you."

A walk will load the bases with two outs, but a base hit will bring home two runs.

The next pitch is heading for the middle of the plate, belt high. I begin my swing, eager to prove myself.

Spencer's windup gives no clue that a changeup is on the way. I try my best to slow my swing, but it's too late. Spence has saved his sucker pitch, his slow ball, just for me. The ball breaks off the bottom edge of my bat and bounces slowly down the third base line. Jack Johnson scoops up the ball with ease and fires it across the infield to first base.

"Way to go, Ace," Three scoffs.

"What's your problem?"

"Made a good impression on Janice, didn't you, Ace?

"I don't care."

But I do care. Do they all think I'm crazy?

I'm the third out, so my new team and I take the field. Convinced that all eyes are on me, I hustle toward second base, stopping abruptly at an imagined line connecting first and second base. I could almost see this line traced in the dirt, like a thin baseline without chalk. Carefully I step over it and turn to face home plate.

The first two batters earn honest base hits. Alex Jones then grounds out to shortstop, advancing the two runners to second and third. Next up, Spencer Hamlin himself hits a high fly that's caught close in by the right fielder. He fires the ball to the catcher to prevent the runner on third from tagging and going home for a score.

After taking a ball and a strike, the next batter, someone I don't know, taps a slow grounder toward me. Moving forward to catch it, I realize I stepped on my imaginary baseline! I stop short and snatch my foot back just as the ball goes past me.

"Way to go, Robin," Three says. "Your new team can be proud of you for that play."

"But I was protecting my powers from you. It's your fault."

"Don't try to blame us for your crazy delusions."

"If my mission is a delusion, you wouldn't be here trying to destroy it."

"We're here to counsel you," One states. "It's a mission of mercy for us."

"So you're trying to save me. Is that it?"

"Yes," One replies. "We're trying to save you from yourself."

"But you're the source of all my problems."

"Guess again," Three says. "It's your vivid imagination. God doesn't give a hoot about you."

A loud voice from the stands brings me back to the game.

"Who's he talking to?"

The grounder that slipped by me allows the runners on second and third to score. My teammates and the crowd are all staring at me.

Coach is on the field, walking toward me.

"Robin," he says. "I'm going to have to take you out of the game."

I see Janice looking at me from across the field. I try to act casual, but her scrutiny leaves me squirming.

What's she thinking?

"Well, the cat's out of the bag now," Three says.

"What do you mean?"

"Janice has discovered you're a real loser."

"I don't care," I say, quite out loud.

"What'd you say?" Coach asks.

"Nothing," I reply. "It's nothing."

I ride home from the game with Coach. He's quiet most of the way, but as we near home, he speaks his mind.

"You're a good ballplayer, Robin," Coach says, as he shifts from second to third gear. "You shouldn't have missed that grounder. What's the problem with the baseline? You acted like it burned your foot. And then you just stood there staring into space."

I stare out the window.

"Don't tell him anything," Two advises. "Remember what happened in the hospital lounge when you talked too much. Henry wanted to send you off to Eastern State."

"You realize, don't you, that your odd routine cost us the game. I wish you'd explain it to me."

"You wouldn't understand."

"Try me."

I can't say anything about my special powers or my mission. No one in my family understands. They all think I'm sick.

"I can't tell you, but it's extremely important, and it must be kept a secret."

"Well can you stop it or put it on hold during our games?"

"No," I mumble.

"Some Holy Cross players think you threw the game."

"What? That's not true!"

"I know, but it did look pretty odd."

I look out the passenger side window at the houses as we pass, tears welling in my eyes.

How did everything in my life change so fast? Is everyone suddenly against me? My old Redeemer teammates are attacking me personally and my new teammates are accusing me of betraying them. They're all against me. Are they conspiring with my demons?

"You understand that I'm going to have to pull you off second base, at least until you can explain what's going on. It wouldn't be fair to the other players if I leave you there."

I nod.

My uncle drops me off at home. Mom and Dad are still at work. Retreating to my room, I put on my favorite record. The lonely, plaintive strains of "Don't fence me in / Let me wonder over yonder / Under starry skies above" echo throughout the house. For once, I'm glad my dad was too busy to come to the game.

13

"Are you going to put me back in the hospital?" I ask, squirming in my chair in front of Dr. Levy's battered oak desk.

I want to run, to hide from the question and the answer.

"He's going to put you in Eastern State," Two warns.

"But he promised he wouldn't."

"And you believe him?" Three derides.

"Dr. Levy wouldn't break his promise."

"Times change," Two explains. "It seems to me you're acting more and more strangely. The business with the cracks and your imaginary powers is bizarre."

"But you've been stealing my powers. If you stop, I'll be all right."

"We're just telling you the truth. You have no special powers. Accept our Master and all your troubles will disappear."

I have the strong sense that my guardian angel is near

again, watching, listening in and taking notes.

"I won't accept Satan."

Talk of Satan makes me short of breath.

"What would make you think that?" Dr. Levy asks.

"What?"

"That I'd put you back in the hospital."

Over the top of his black horn-rimmed glasses, Dr. Levy's piercing gray eyes watch me closely.

"I just want to be sure."

The smoke and foul odor of Dr. Levy's cigar surrounds me, irritating my nostrils and eyes. He always jokes that they are cheap Cuban cigars, but my dad says there is no such thing. I wonder if a cigar has to smell bad to be good.

"Your mother tells me you're avoiding cracks and tapping your toes behind you. Are these some of your new defenses?"

So, my mother told him. Is this going to get me in trouble?

"What defenses?"

My chest tightens. It's getting harder to breathe.

"See, even Dr. Levy thinks all that monkey business is a waste of time," Two interjects.

"Dr. Levy has never said that I'm ill."

"He put you in the hospital, didn't he?" Three challenges.

"He put me in the hospital so I could get some rest while

they figured out how much medication I should be taking."

"That's a rather fine distinction," One counters.

I hug myself against the chill.

"You'll never give up, will you? Are you stupid? I know you're lying to me."

"Robin, are you all right?" Dr. Levy asks.

"Oh. They aren't defenses."

"Well, then, if they aren't defenses, what are they?"

"They're how I do battle with Satan and his demons."

"Aren't you also protecting something as well?" Dr. Levy asks, leaning back in his chair.

It squeaks loudly, but he doesn't seem to notice. Whenever I see him, he's completely absorbed in my situation.

"It's pretty complicated."

"You're protecting the new powers you use to fight off Satan and his demons, am I right?"

How does Dr. Levy know that?

"The boy is certainly dense," Three snarls. "He's never going to figure out he has no special powers. Even Levy knows that."

"You're wrong. You can badger me all you want, but I know better."

"Well, just remember that our Benefactor would never desert you as God has."

"God hasn't deserted me," I insist.

"Excuse me, Robin, but the three of us are here talking to you," One says. "When was the last time God said one word to you? Have his angels stepped in to protect you or given you advice?"

"From whom are you protecting your powers?" Dr. Levy asks.

"What?"

"From whom are you protecting your powers?"

"From Satan and his demons."

"How do they threaten your powers?"

"When I step on cracks, they are able to steal some of my powers."

"Do they do anything else?"

"Yes."

"What else do they do?"

"They're constantly trying to convince me God hasn't given me any special powers. That He's abandoned me."

"Do you think God has abandoned you?"

"God would never do that."

"Then why do you care about what they say?"

"They represent Satan so I must deny their claims. They're a threat to my faith and my salvation. And they nag me constantly."

"Your mother says you're often preoccupied or withdrawn.

Does it have anything to do with your demons nagging you?"

Dr. Levy takes a drink of coffee, which he always keeps on his desk in an oddly shaped, green, ceramic mug his son made for him at summer camp.

"I'm not withdrawn. I'm just busy."

"Talking with your demons?"

"Yes. Denying all of their false claims requires a lot of time and effort."

"Is that where the toe tapping comes in?"

"The toe tapping is related."

"How does that work?"

"I found out that if I tap my toes behind me after stepping on a crack, it seals the crack. Then my demons can't drain away my powers."

"So avoiding cracks and tapping your toes are intended to accomplish specific objectives."

"Yes."

Dr. Levy waits.

"Mom says that I have to stop doing things like tapping my toes or you'll put me back in the hospital."

"Why would she say that?"

"I think she wants me to stop because my behavior embarrasses her."

"You're probably right," Dr. Levy adds. "Most people

probably find your behavior odd."

"If they don't understand, it's because they don't know the truth."

"Does that surprise you?"

"Not anymore."

"Well, to answer your original question, I've told your mother I'm not putting you back in the hospital."

He told my mother! No one *tells* my mother! Dr. Levy isn't betraying me after all.

"The shrink is in trouble now," Three blurts out.

"What do you mean?"

"He's taking your mother on," Two observes. "That's going to mean trouble."

"Mom's pretty upset with me," I say.

"You're right, of course," Dr. Levy replies. "She finds your behavior embarrassing. But that's not a good enough reason for me to put you back in the hospital."

I feel a weight lift from my shoulders.

"Mom's going to have a fit. She won't let it go."

"She'll just have to learn to live with it. I told her not to interrupt you anymore," Dr. Levy continues.

"Why?" I ask.

"Why did I tell your mother not to interrupt you?" Dr. Levy asks with a puzzled look on his face.

"No, why does it upset her so much when I'm busy defending myself?"

"She thinks you're hallucinating."

"What's that?"

"She thinks you're hearing voices and seeing things that are not real."

"So the real reason she's upset is that she thinks I'm mentally ill. Isn't that right?"

"Your mother is extremely concerned about you."

"What about softball?" I stammer.

"What about it?"

"I can't play when my demons are harassing me and I must protect myself."

"And, like your mother, you'll have to learn to live with that."

"But, I want to play softball."

"Then you'll have to come up with some other way to protect your powers. We all must live with the consequences of our behavior."

Dr. Levy leans forward to look directly at me. It isn't a look of disapproval, but one of kindness, as if he knows this is asking a lot.

"I'm going to increase your medication."

"The medication already makes me tired and weak."

"Some things are more important."

"Like what?"

"I think an increase in your medication may help you. We'll try it and then next week we'll talk about how it affects you."

"If you think it'll help."

"I've also suggested an alternate sport to your parents that would be better than softball for right now."

Better for me!

"What I really want is to play softball."

"We've already discussed that. In the meantime, I think you might like my suggestion."

"What's this other sport?"

"Croquet, anyone?" Three jeers. "Or, how about horseshoes? It's bound to be something stupid. I'd let him know right off that you're not interested."

"I'm going to let your parents tell you," Dr. Levy says.

He's grinning from ear to ear like the Cheshire Cat from *Alice in Wonderland.*

Is he teasing or tormenting me?

"Softball is what I do for the summer," I reply, looking at the floor.

"Come on, son, wake up," my father says, shaking me

gently. "Get some clothes on. Wear your jeans and work boots. Uncle Ray is waiting for us."

"Where is he?"

"He's at home. We're going to pick him up on the way," Father replies.

"Where are we going?"

"I can't tell you. It's a surprise."

"Why is Uncle Ray coming with us?"

"I can't tell you that either."

Father leaves my bedroom and heads for the kitchen as I get out of bed and start to get dressed. My alarm clock shows 6:30 a.m.

It's Sunday morning. Shouldn't we be getting ready for church? What's all this about?

"This is a mistake, Bob," Mother says. "You'll spoil him. He shouldn't be rewarded for skipping over cracks and tapping his toes. He's got to learn to stop that sort of behavior."

Oddly, Mother, who's in the kitchen, makes no attempt to lower her voice, almost as if she wants me to overhear, as if she is trying to tell me something.

"Horsefeathers! You're the one who insisted we take Robin to the shrink," Father replies, his voice reflecting his impatience. "We're paying the doctor a lot of money. I think we should do what he says, at least until we see if it helps."

See if it helps? Helps what?

"Your mother is going to dump Dr. Levy," Three gloats.

"She's already starting to make her case."

"My dad won't let her."

"Right, like he stopped her from taking you to the shrink in the first place?"

"You'll see. My dad means business this time."

"Good luck, pal. Dr. Levy's on his way out."

I can't lose Dr. Levy now. God, please help me.

"This is going to be way too expensive," Mother says.

"I don't care about the money if it'll help Robin."

"Notice how your father always tries to buy his way out of things," Two observes. **"He'll spend money on you, but he doesn't have time to do anything with you."**

"He's going out with me this morning, isn't he?"

"He's willing to skip church, but he's going to go back to the store this afternoon and leave you on your own," Three adds.

The store again. I hate the store.

"I don't see how spoiling the boy is going to help," Mother continues. "Marvin's got a point, you know. It'll set a bad example for his cousins."

"You mean it'll make things harder for Marvin."

I remember how "helpful" Uncle Marvin had been in the hospital.

Marvin deserves a little trouble of his own. No! I mustn't

think that way. It's a sin to wish bad things for someone. God, please forgive me.

"Your uncle Marvin deserves all the trouble he gets," **Three says.**

"I won't wish trouble on Marvin. He means well."

"He's telling your mother she's wasting her money on Dr. Levy," **Two insists,** *"that you need discipline."*

"This latest scheme of your shrink has got your mother upset," **One adds.** *"She's going to dump the quack."*

"You lie. You can't scare me."

"What this means for Marvin is beside the point," Mother replies. "But remember, he's raising four boys and they always want whatever Robin gets."

"It's a sport, Lora. It's not going to spoil the boy. Let Robin have a little fun. With all his troubles, it seems to me that he deserves that much. He can work to cover the expenses."

"Where is he going to work?' Mother asks. 'You've seen how he behaves around other people."

"He can work in the store."

"Bob, he can't work with customers."

"He can work in back with Frank."

"Well, I think it's a bad idea. The boy needs discipline."

"What'd we tell you?" **Two gloats.** *"Your mother is listening to your uncle Marvin. Dr. Levy is on his way out."*

The idea of losing Dr. Levy leaves me in a cold sweat.

Having gotten dressed, I go to the kitchen.

"Dad, I'm ready to go."

"Now wait just a minute," Mother snaps, "You can't go out looking like that. What's wrong with you? You used to keep your hair combed."

"Ah, Mom..."

"Why is your mother always nagging you about how you look?" Two asks.

"You march right back into the bathroom and comb your hair. Have you brushed your teeth?"

"No."

"Now she's not only ashamed of how you act, but how you look. Your mother's no help to you. Ignore her. I wouldn't be surprised if she dumps you along with your shrink."

"Mother loves me."

"She loves you like your father does—when it's convenient," Two counters. "Your strange behavior is making things inconvenient for your mother. This crazy 'mission' of yours is going to alienate her."

"You lie."

"Give up on this imaginary mission of yours," One demands. "Accept our Leader."

"Never!"

I shake my head in denial.

"What's come over you?" Mother continues. "Now do as I say. Get busy and brush your teeth and wash your face. And while you're at it, put on a clean shirt. The one you've got on looks like you've been wearing it for a week. Besides, it clashes with your pants."

I return to my room to get a clean shirt, wondering if my mother might actually dump me.

"I tell you, Bob, the boy needs discipline."

We pick up Uncle Ray a half hour later. He brings a thermos of hot coffee and three empty coffee mugs with him. I sit in the middle of the bench seat in my father's pickup, with the gear shift rising from the floor between my knees. We head north on Division Street toward Newport, about forty-five miles from Spokane.

"Why are we going to Newport on Sunday morning?"

"I can't tell you," my Father says, smiling. "Remember, it's a surprise. Now drink your coffee."

Mother would have a fit if she'd known they are giving me coffee. I don't understand her complaint. She has drunk coffee since she was five years old because she is allergic to whole milk. I take a sip and don't say anything more. It makes me feel like one of the men.

Shortly after passing through Newport, we turn left onto a double set of tracks leading up and over a small rise. Alfalfa fields border the lane all the way to the farmhouse in the small valley below. It's surrounded by several outbuildings that prove to be stables.

A tall, thin man in overalls and muck boots comes out to greet us.

"You Ray Casselman?" The farmer asks, pulling off his cowboy hat and wiping the sweat from his brow with the sleeve of his shirt.

My uncle nods.

"Name's Henderson, but you know that. You're here about Shady then?"

Shady! Who's Shady?

"Yep, you haven't sold her yet, have you?"

"No, but it's good you've come early. I'm getting a lot of calls."

"Then I'm glad we came right out."

"You hear about Shady from Guy?" the farmer asked.

"Yes, Guy's my brother," Uncle Ray answers.

"Casselman, same last name, I figured as much. Guy's a good farmer, just had some bad luck. Someday he'll get another herd of Holsteins."

"He's trying to work our father's homestead. It's good land."

"I guess that makes you good folks. Won't let Shady go to just anyone."

"That's what Guy told me," Ray replies.

"Well, let's take a look at her then," Henderson says.

We make our way into the nearest stable.

"She's in the third stall and as fine a piece of horseflesh as you'll ever see."

Horseflesh!

I step on a crack between the wide planks that are used for flooring in the stable. Stopping to tap my toes, I look up to find Henderson watching me closely.

"You make trouble everywhere you go," Three snickers.

Uncle Ray enters the stall and begins to examine Shady, looking at her hoofs, checking her legs, running his hand down her back, and looking admiringly at the arch in her neck. He opens her mouth and examines her teeth.

Shady is light gray, almost white.

She's so big! What if she gets loose? She could trample us all!

"Eight years you say?" Ray asks, swatting at the flies buzzing around his head.

"Eight come late June."

"Look's about right," Ray mumbles to himself.

"She's what," Ray asks, "about fifteen hands?"

"Fifteen exactly," Henderson responds.

Shady stirs uneasily at the presence of strangers, neighing and tossing her head. She could be fifteen feet tall as far as I'm concerned. I shrink back when she stamps her hooves. She looks nasty. I want to run for the door.

"Guess what?" Three says. "The kid's got something right. This is one mean horse. I'm taking bets on how long it takes this horse to kill him."

"Be quiet," One admonishes.

"She's a little skittish about the head," Henderson continues.

"Why's that?"

"Bottle broke by an old wrangler. The old ways die hard, you know."

"You said on the phone that she's fully trained," Uncle Ray says.

"Yep, she's a fine cattle horse. Mostly cutting and roping, both on the ranch and in rodeo competition. She's been shown in rodeos for bravery too, which is pretty unusual. But she hasn't been ridden much lately. She'll take some work."

"See. Even Henderson admits she might be dangerous," Three warns. "You're in for real trouble."

"Shut up! One says.

"And just how is she going to kill me? I've never seen her before today. If Uncle Ray buys her, she'll be his problem."

"He's not listening very well, is he?" Two says.

"How does she handle?" Uncle Ray asks.

"She handles like a dream for an experienced cowpoke. She's a Morab."

"What's a Morab?" Father inquires.

Henderson looked at my father with disdain, spitting out a plug of tobacco.

"It's a cross between an Arabian and a Morgan," Uncle Ray explains quietly. "It's one of the best combinations for a working cattle horse, smart, spirited, quick and physically powerful."

"She's for you, I assume," Henderson says, looking at Uncle Ray.

"No, she's for the boy here."

She's for the boy here? What's Uncle Ray talking about? I'm the only boy here.

"I don't know about that," Henderson replies, looking surprised. "Do you think the boy can handle this much horse?"

Is this Dr. Levy's surprise?

Henderson's gaze is now fixed on me. He's seen me tap my toes and stamp my feet, which has obviously puzzled him. Clearly his promise not to sell the horse to just anyone is not an idle comment.

He takes out his penknife and cuts off another chunk of tobacco.

I feel my heart sink. Henderson's description of Shady leaves me frightened, but now I want her badly, a cattle horse of my own, a dream horse.

"The farmer doesn't want you to have his horse," Three taunts me. *"This is a lucky break. Just get out of here."*

"I'll teach him to handle her," Uncle Ray says firmly.

"Well, you'd better teach him good and watch him close. If Shady senses he's a greenhorn, she'll give him a rough ride.

And she knows a cowpoke when she carries one."

The thought of owning Shady is exciting. I could be the Lone Ranger! The Cisco Kid! I'll buy a scabbard, a Winchester Model 94, a lariat, saddle bags, and a bed roll. But what if I can't handle her? I could be thrown in the woods and break my back. They might not find me for days.

"My point exactly," Three says. "No wonder your mother thinks this scheme is a bad idea. Tell them you don't want the horse."

"The boy will be fine," Uncle Ray insists.

I rub my sweaty palms on my blue jeans.

Shady is a man's horse and I'm going to be a man about all this. I've become a good game fisherman. I can become a good cowpoke.

"Well, that's your business," Henderson continues. "The price is four-fifty."

"What do you think, Bob?" Uncle Ray turns and asks my father.

"It's fine with me, as long as you teach him to ride proper."

"That's just like your father. He's going to buy the horse, but isn't going to ride with you. He's just too busy with the store. He's going to leave that to your uncle Ray."

I have no reply. My excitement is now mixed with disappointment. I had hoped that my father was finally going to take an interest in what I'm doing.

"I've also got a good bridle and working saddle," Henderson adds. "It fits her well. Nothing fancy, with a roping horn and second cinch, but good leather."

"How much?"

"One-fifty."

Uncle Ray looks at my father.

"Sounds fine," Father says.

"You might need to use a tougher bit for the boy here," Henderson cautions.

"We'll take care of that," Ray says.

"Cash money?" Henderson is not really asking.

"Cash," my father replies.

14

"So how do you like my idea for a new sport?" Dr. Levy asks, trying to mask his excitement.

"What idea?"

"What do you mean, 'What idea'?"

Determined to play this for all it is worth, I say nothing.

"Well?"

I remain silent for a minute longer.

"You don't mean, the horse, do you?"

Dr. Levy's eyes light up. He smiles broadly.

"Yes, the horse, of course, the horse! Do you like him?"

Thrilled about Shady, I feel like I did when I was released from the hospital, excited and grateful to be alive despite my present agonies.

"As I recall, when you left the hospital, you were skipping down the sidewalk with joy," Three recounts. "Do you remember what happened next?"

"I fell."

"You ripped your pants, bloodied your nose, and skinned your knee."

"So what?

"How have your expectations for a new beginning worked out so far?"

"Not well."

"This will be the same. The horse isn't going to change anything unless you accept our Master first," Two replies.

"This time it will be different."

"Robin?"

"What?"

"Do you like your horse?"

I can't hide my enthusiasm about Shady any longer. I'm certain that she represents the new beginning, the future I want, and much, much more.

"She's terrific."

"Don't be a fool," Two counters. "Shady is a dumb animal. She'll bring you nothing but work and misery."

"What kind of a horse did you get? Is she black?"

"No, Shady's light gray, almost white with black markings.

160

She's like Silver, you know, the Lone Ranger's horse."

"Is she trained?"

"She's a cattle horse." My chest swells with pride.

"What does she do?"

"She's a cutting and roping horse. You know, like real cowboys have."

I picture myself in the midst of a cattle drive, scrub as far as the eye can see, the sweat, dust, and backbreaking work, but free on the open range, even free of my demons' constant harassment.

Don't fence me in / let me wander over yonder / with starry skies above, I sing quietly to myself.

"Will you learn to rope bulls and all that?"

"Nobody ropes a bull and lives to tell about it. Uncle Guy has promised to show me how to rope calves."

"Haven't you noticed there are few cowboys around anymore?" Three jeers. "There's a reason."

"There are lots of cowboys. Every cattle ranch in the West has cowboys."

"And they all ride . . . uh . . . drive jeeps."

"There's no ball and chain on the open range. I can roam wherever I want with a horse like Shady."

"True," Two agrees. "And you can rest easy. We'll be your advisers wherever you go for the rest of your life."

Oh my God! Is he saying they'll never leave me?

I struggle to get my breath.

"What does she cut?" Dr. Levy asks.

Dr. Levy is definitely a city slicker.

"She's trained to separate cattle," I reply, "to cut a specific steer out of the herd."

I wish she could separate me from my demons.

"Have you ridden her yet?"

"No."

"When are you going to start?"

"My uncle Ray…"

"I repeat, the horse is going to kill you," Three growls.

"Stop interrupting me. You've no idea what's going to happen, so lay off with the stupid advice."

"Your uncle Ray…?" Dr. Levy prompts.

"My uncle Ray is going to give me my first riding lesson next Sunday. Guy will work with me after that."

"Are you excited?"

"I don't know if I can wait for the week."

"What about your father?"

"He usually works, but he's going out to the farm with Uncle Ray and me early that Sunday morning," I reply with some pride.

"Isn't that just swell," Three mocks me. "He's going to

spend an entire day with you. "

"*Leave my dad out of this,* " I reply to Three. "*He made all the arrangements for Shady.* "

"Is your dad also going to learn how to ride?" Dr. Levy asks.

"Not a chance. He says that with all the work at the store, he won't have time."

"What about church?"

"Oh, I'll be in church this Sunday. Mother doesn't like the idea that I'm going to miss church next week though, but my father says it's the only day he can go."

"One lousy Sunday," Three says. "That's pathetic."

"So, you won't be riding this week. What are you going to do on the farm?"

"Guy is going to show me how to take care of Shady."

"Once you've learned, will you have a chance to ride her often?"

"She'll be the death of you," Three insists once again.

"Lots, I hope. Dad's arranged for me to spend the week on the farm. Mother's going to take me out after church on Sundays and pick me up Friday mornings before my appointment with you."

"You'll be spending weekends at home then?"

"Yes! Mother insists I attend church."

Dr. Levy makes a note.

"What will you do on Friday afternoons and Saturdays?"

"I'm going to work in the produce department at the store. It's how I'm going to earn the money to buy Shady's winter feed."

"No doubt your father will pay you union scale?" Three jeers.

"I'm not a member of the union. I'll be an apprentice."

"So he's going to shave his costs and make a little more money."

"I'm going to learn the trade."

"You like my idea then?" Dr. Levy asks.

"Yes. I think its dynamite! But, I can't let it distract me from my mission."

"You've never told me about your mission," Dr. Levy says as if I'd simply commented about last week's weather.

"I've got to warn you," One snaps. "Telling your doctor about this mission you've concocted is not a good idea."

"But I want him to know. He's the only one who understands what's happening to me."

"I don't believe my ears," Two says, sounding hurt. "We understand. Haven't we been through thick and thin with you?"

"You lie to me. Go away."

"I've never told you because I don't fully understand my mission yet. Not everything has been disclosed."

"Does your mission involve your special powers?" Dr. Levy asks.

"Yes."

"But that's a horse of a different color," Dr. Levy says.

I laugh. Sometimes Dr. Levy is funny.

"Don't get too friendly with the good doctor," Two warns. "He'll betray you in the end."

"I trust Dr. Levy."

"And I warn you," One retorts. "It'll cost him dearly if he interferes with our Master's plan for you."

"Are you threatening Dr. Levy?"

I close my eyes, put my hands over my ears, and shake my head from side to side in disbelief and denial.

"He's not part of our Leader's plan for you. No one will be allowed to disrupt your destiny. If anyone stops your progress, they can expect no mercy."

"But he's just been trying to..."

"Why do you think we've warned you again and again not to get the doctor or anyone else you care about or trust involved?"

God, help me. I'm here to do your will, not to hurt others. My demons block my prayers to you. Can they also harm others because of what I do or don't do?

I use my handkerchief to wipe the sweat that has suddenly broken out on my forehead. I slump in my chair. The added burden seems more than I can possibly bear.

"Tell me something?" Dr. Levy says. "Is there any pattern to how you tap your toes?"

"I always tap them four times. I start with my right toe, follow with two taps of my left and then finish with one more tap of my right."

"You mustn't tell him anything else," One cautions.

"I have to tell someone."

"We've warned you of the potential consequences," One adds.

I've got to be careful about whom I talk to and how much I tell them. Yet surely God will protect those who help me with my mission just as He'll protect me. Suddenly I sense the presence of my guardian angel so strongly that it takes my breath away.

"Why do you do this?" Dr. Levy asks.

"I do it to preserve the symmetry of the universe," I admit, my voice weak and wavering. "Starting and ending with my right toe means that I'm starting and ending at the right hand of God."

"Why is symmetry so important?"

"That's one part of my mission I do understand. I'm supposed to maintain the balance of good and evil in the universe. I can't allow evil to take over. That means I have to preserve symmetry. I've got to protect my powers because they're essential to maintaining the right balance. I'm quite certain I'll need them for other parts of my mission too."

"There is no good or evil in the universe," One says. "Unfortunate things happen because God is jealous of our Benefactor. God's always trying to discredit him. God's neglect is what put you in the hospital."

"Why wouldn't you favor the good?" Dr. Levy asks. "I mean just create more good than evil and be done with it?"

"I can't create good by myself. Only God can do that.

When I fail God, I cause evil. Others create evil as well. Some do it on purpose like my demons. All this evil needs to be offset with good. If mankind, even the universe, is to survive, there must always be more good than evil."

"How do you maintain this balance?"

"For now, by tapping my toes, stamping my feet, and by the way I walk."

"Tell me, Doctor, does he really think tapping his toes and the like is going to make a difference?" Three scoffs.

"Dr. Levy can't hear you."

"If you can't create good this way, how do these behaviors help? How do you offset evil and preserve the balance?"

"When I tap my right toe I draw on the good that God has created."

"How does that work?"

"I'm kind of like a lightning rod."

"I don't believe the nonsense he comes up with," Three jeers. "Now he's a lightning rod for God. How ridiculous can this get?"

"So in a way you're tapping into God's powers."

"Yes. And the power I call down from God also restores my own powers."

"He's beginning to sound like a public utility!" Three jokes. The other demons laugh.

"What happens when you tap your left foot?"

"I destroy evil. So, you see the right stands for good, the left for evil. There are other ways of doing this, I know. I need to learn what they are. Continuing to learn is an important part of my mission."

"Is he ever confused," Three says. "He thinks he controls the universe."

"I don't control the universe. God does."

"Then what's all this baloney about maintaining the balance of good and evil?"

"That's part of my mission. I'm only one of many that God has given this responsibility."

"God's far too jealous to share his powers with anyone," Three exclaims.

"That's not what I've been taught!"

"Has it ever occurred to you that your education just might be a conglomeration of nonsense, of lies?"

"And you're lying to me right now. I'm tired of you trying to twist the truth."

"Will you explain your special walk to me," Dr. Levy asks. "We haven't discussed this."

"It's something new I'm developing to use in times of crisis. I'm still testing it out to make sure it works."

"Can you describe it to me?"

"When I walk, I never let my left foot get ahead of my right so evil can't get ahead of good."

"What do you mean, 'you never let your left foot get ahead of your right'?"

I get up to demonstrate.

"I take a full stride with my right foot like this. Then when I bring my left foot forward, I shorten my stride, setting my foot down next to my right. As you can see, my left foot is never placed ahead of my right. I won't allow it."

I walk haltingly around the perimeter of the room.

"Isn't that awkward?"

"I only use it in emergencies. You know, when good and evil get way out of balance."

"What do people say when you use it?"

"People who don't know me think I'm crippled. Most of my relatives, like Uncle Marvin, think I'm doing it to get attention. But I'm not going to let what they think get in the way of my mission."

Dr. Levy nods as if he understands fully.

"I'm beginning to think Robin is a mental cripple," Two says.

"Why has God selected you to help maintain the balance of good and evil?"

"You stupid shrink," Three snaps. "It's all in Robin's imagination."

"I repeat, Dr. Levy can't hear you."

"If he could, he might learn something," Two says.

"I don't know. I just know that I must do this. It is to make sure that when God ends the world there'll be enough good to cancel out evil. Remember, in heaven, there'll be no evil. So it has to be cancelled out so heaven can continue to exist."

15

"This time you're going in for the service," Mother announces as we pull into the parking lot behind Holy Cross. "We're going to be in God's house so you won't need any defenses. Is that clear?"

Oh God, I hope she's right. I'm exhausted from defending myself from Satan. I desperately need a break.

"It's important for people to see that you're a good Christian, that your faith is strong, so behave yourself. And remember, Carl is with us. The congregation will know by now that he's studying for the ministry. You don't want to embarrass him."

"This is not the time for rest. We're trying to toughen you up," Three says. *"Think of it as boot camp. No pain, no gain. You're in training for a magnificent destiny."*

"Like Mother just said, God won't let you enter His house. He'll protect me from all of you."

"Do you think that going into a church building is going to make any difference?" Two asks.

God, please make it so. Please block Satan and his demons from entering. Give me rest.

"He's a fool," Three replies.

"Eventually he'll figure out that God doesn't want him," Two replies.

"Don't be dragging your feet," Mother commands as we start up the walk to the front of the church.

Fortunately, the squares in the sidewalk leading to the entrance are large. I adjust the length of my stride to avoid the cracks between them without being too obvious. Carl is the only one who notices.

"Are you all right, kiddo?" he asks. "You're as white as a sheet."

"Yes. I'll be just fine."

We step inside the vestibule where my parents spot my uncle Ray and my aunt Ester.

"Carl, please go in and save us a pew," Mother says. "Take Robin with you. Your father and I need to talk to Ray and Ester."

Carl nods to Mother and gives me a gentle shove.

The floor is covered with linoleum tile, just like the store! I must be careful. But wait! Mother said my demons aren't allowed in God's house. They won't be able to steal my powers.

With confidence, I deliberately step on a crack to prove my point. What feels like a violent electric shock runs up and down my leg. I can feel my powers draining away at an alarming rate.

Suddenly feeling faint and nauseated, I snatch my foot

back. Staggering, I put my hand over my mouth. I'm now terrified of the cracks that are everywhere.

"Take it easy, Bub," Carl says. "If you throw up this morning's bacon and eggs, it'll make a real mess."

Obviously my powers can be lost even in the absence of my demons. But why are these cracks so much more dangerous?

"It's not safe for me here."

"Don't worry," Carl says, "I'll protect you."

I tiptoe up the center aisle of the sanctuary.

"What's he doing?" a little girl asks her mother as I passed.

She sounds just like the brat in the store.

"Shush," her mother whispers, putting an index finger across her lips.

My concentration broken, I look up to see the questioning eyes of the congregation jumping back and forth between Carl and me. Carl's acting as if this is nothing out of the ordinary.

They're passing judgment on me. They don't know that I'm struggling to preserve my powers and that all this is part of my mission. If I don't succeed, they will perish.

I step on more cracks and begin to tap my toes behind me to prevent my powers from draining away, taking great care to ensure that my toes don't strike additional cracks.

"What's he doing now?" a woman on the aisle asks. "He shouldn't be doing that in the Lord's house."

She doesn't understand. I'm doing God's will. I'm maintaining the balance of good and evil.

"You're not welcome here."

It's a woman's voice!

"God doesn't want you here."

I can tell that this second woman isn't saying this out loud! She's thinking it and putting her thoughts directly into my mind much as Satan does, except Satan mimics my thinking voice. This woman is using her own voice. Yet because she is not speaking out loud, I have no way of knowing who she is.

"Get out. We don't want you in our church. Leave."

Now it's a man's thoughts.

I turn to Carl, whispering. "Do you hear them?"

"Do I hear who?"

"Do you hear the voices telling us to get out?"

"Some of the parishioners are muttering," Carl replies, "but I can't make out what anyone is saying."

"No, I mean the man and woman who told me to leave. They are forcing their wishes into my mind."

"You're making this up, right?"

It has to be the parishioners. They're transmitting their thoughts, their commands, directly into my mind. How can this be? Satan's demons must have somehow invited them in without my knowledge.

Their thoughts seem to be entering my mind so easily. I can fight off Satan and his demons within me, but I don't know how to defend myself against a large congregation, a congregation that's depositing its thoughts in my mind from the outside, especially when I don't know which members are doing this.

"You must leave. Your behavior is unacceptable."

"No!"

I've done nothing wrong. It's essential that I protect my powers. I can't let others put thoughts into my mind. I must control my own thinking.

I stumble and step on even more cracks, my powers rapidly bleeding out of me. My skin stings as if I had fallen into a patch of nettles and I don't know if I can continue. I start to turn around to leave, but Carl pushes me forward.

I'm doing God's will. Doesn't the congregation understand its intrusions are dangerous to me?

"You don't belong here."

"No! That's not right."

I must use my special powers to stop these attacks. I focus all my mental energy in opposition, and since I don't know who is putting these thoughts directly into my mind, I direct this energy to all the members of the church in attendance.

"I am only doing God's will. You must understand. I have a mission from God."

"You're right . . . his behavior . . . is . . . inappropriate," I hear snatches of a woman speaking.

They are no longer even trying to hide what they think! They're now talking to each other out loud.

The parishioners are no longer whispering, no longer making any attempt to be discreet. And they continue to force their thoughts and commands into my mind.

"I can't believe his parents brought him into our church," another says.

Who's turned the congregation against me?

I feel the presence of my guardian angel.

My head is spinning in confusion.

I must get out of God's house.

"No!" Satan says.

God, help me. Satan is involved in this. They're trying to drive me out of your house, to deny me the rest I need and you have promised.

"Give it a rest," Three commands. "God is not listening to you."

Oh, no! Satan's demons are here. They can get into God's house. My mother was wrong!

Seeing the pew at the front vacant, I execute a right turn with military precision, successfully avoiding the cracks. Moving to the middle, I sit down. Carl sits next to me.

"Don't pay any attention to them," Carl whispers. "People always talk and stare when new members show up."

He slugs my shoulder as brothers often do.

"You can't hear them, can you?"

"We're new," Carl says. "They'll get tired of talking about us in a couple of weeks. Just ignore them."

Carl obviously can't hear the angry thoughts the congregation is forcing into my mind.

More and more parishioners are sending their unspoken commands. Each voice is different from the others.

I focus all my mental energies once again, sending my thoughts to the entire congregation.

"I'm doing God's will. You must understand that this is part of my mission."

I can hear the buzz of conversation behind my back.

"Well, you've heard about what happened…acting weird on the field. His mother… worried…but why in the world did she bring him into the church?"

Carl turns to glare.

Acid rises in my throat. The chapel turns cold.

"Did you see…he walks…looks like some pagan ritual… can't believe his parents brought him into…"

"You can't possibly be a Christian. Get out of our church."

"No, this is most certainly not true," I reply under my breath. "I've been a Christian all my life."

"On the contrary, you've always been one of us," One taunts me.

"Never!"

"It's quite simple," One continues. "God doesn't want you and he especially doesn't want you here. He's talking to you through his flock."

"God, why have you let my demons into your house? Why aren't you protecting me?"

"God doesn't care about you and no amount of praying is going to help," Two says. "He's not listening. And just for the record, we go where we choose. God has no control over us."

Doubt gnaws away at the edges of my faith.

My parents sit down on either side of me just as the organist starts to play. Carl sits nearest to the aisle, next to Mother.

"Get out of the church while you still can, before they decide to stone you," One pleads.

The liturgy starts with its ritualistic rhythms. Pastor Hienes chants and the congregation replies.

Reverend Voelcker never chanted. This ritual is clearly aimed at me. They're trying to drive me out. But my mission is from God. Why would His congregations do this?

"Just as we said," Two interjects, "God's flock is doing his dirty work."

Like claps of thunder, the music and singing pounds on me. I think my head will burst. The room spins around. I fade in and out of awareness.

Then everything goes still.

I no longer know where we are in the liturgy and have no idea how much time has passed.

Is God stepping in to protect me from…

God has abandoned you," Two says.

The organ booms as the congregation begins to sing.

"Rock of Ages / Cleft for me…"

Their singing amplifies the drumming chords of the music, both reverberating in my head.

I try to block out the congregation's voices, their singing and the pounding music. I writhe in my seat. As hard as I try, I can't block out the parishioners' thoughts. I close my eyes and lean forward, placing my head on my knees.

"God, why aren't you protecting me? What about the rest you promised? Why have you let Satan and his demons in? Why have you let them turn the congregation against me?"

"Robin, sit up," Mother whispers.

The room grows even colder. I shake with the chill.

Mother tugs at my shoulders.

"Robin, you can't continue to act this way."

Throughout the remainder of the service, Mother tries to coax me into participating, but I can't. My hands over my ears, my head on my knees, I hide like a tortoise, withdrawn and silent, not moving.

We leave immediately after the service. I tiptoe and tap my way down the center aisle of the chapel, through the foyer, out of the building, and down the walk outside. The parishioners watch my every move, but keep their distance.

Driving in silence, Mother drops Father off at the store, and then we start for Guy's farm. Once alone with me, Mother speaks her mind.

"And just what was that all about?"

"It's the new church."

"What are you talking about?"

"They don't want me."

"Who doesn't want you?"

"The congregation doesn't want me."

"That's nonsense."

"We warned you not to go into the church," Two says.

"They made their wishes quite clear."

My hand goes to my chest. Mother quickly reaches out to pull it away.

"If you think this is going to get you out of going to church, you're sadly mistaken."

I look out the window, saying nothing.

Why doesn't Mother listen to me? Why does she just assume the fault is mine, that I can control what's happening to me?

"And don't think just because you're getting next Sunday off to start your riding lessons that you'll be spending all your Sundays on the farm. You need to be in church."

"Your mother is your worst enemy," Two observes. "You must free yourself from your family."

"Whatever you say, Mother."

"I know the new church seems strange, but you'll get used to it. I saw lots of boys and girls your age." Mother's voice is now much softer.

"I don't think strange is the right term," Two states. "Toxic seems more accurate."

"They hate me."

"What?"

"They all hate me."

"Who are you talking about?"

"All the parishioners at Holy Cross."

"Robin! That's nonsense. You should be ashamed of yourself."

"Your mother will never understand," One says. "Listen to our counsel."

"Like you're ashamed of me?" I say, turning to look at Mother. "I tell you God does not attend that church."

My mother's face goes ashen. Fear flashes in her eyes.

Now that the church has been corrupted, I must find a new place of refuge. Where does God want me to turn? Is this an important step in my mission?

I look out the window at the landscape as we speed through the countryside. I feel as if I'm racing headlong down the highway toward some grand finale, traveling so fast that everyday sights and events, like the pines along the side of the road, are a blur that give no hint of my destination.

If I'm to complete my mission, it's essential that I keep the thoughts of others out of my mind.

"So how was the week on the farm?" Dr. Levy asks.

I double over in my chair.

Even though I expect him to ask, Dr. Levy's question hits me like a punch in the gut.

Dr. Levy waits patiently.

"The first . . . the first night was . . . was hard."

"Why was that?"

I jerk upright.

"It was be...because of Sunday...morning," I gasp.

"What happened Sunday morning?"

The trauma still fresh in my mind, Dr. Levy's direct questions take me back into the church. His voice seems distorted like the chanting of the liturgy. I can hear the drumming of the music, the singing and the commands of some church members. Even though I'm in the safety of Dr. Levy's office, a tremor goes through me. I can't hide from the vivid recollections of what happened in the church service last Sunday.

"Tell the good doctor what happened," Two challenges. "God rejected you. The parishioners only delivered the message."

I clench my fists and pound on the arms of my chair.

"You know that's a vicious lie. You have led them all astray. You've destroyed my refuge."

"Robin, are you all right?"

I take a deep breath and force myself to face Dr. Levy. His eyes reveal his concern.

182

"Can we just talk about the farm for now?"

"Yes, of course."

"I was still pretty upset Sunday night. I kept waking up my cousin Derris."

"So you didn't sleep well?"

"I was up and down all night."

"You were up and down?"

"I was pacing around the house. I even went outside for a while. It didn't help."

"It sounds like you were quite anxious."

"I couldn't stay in bed. My skin was crawling and I was sick to my stomach."

"I assume it wasn't the farm that troubled you?"

I stiffen and grab the arms of my chair.

"Tell him the whole story," Two says. "Tell him your God has repudiated you."

"I'll tell him no such thing."

"We'll eventually need to talk about Sunday morning," Dr. Levy continues, "but for the moment, let's stick with the farm."

"What do you want to know?"

"How was the rest of the week?"

"Derris and I were tired all day Monday, but things got better after that."

"What was better about it?"

"I'm learning a lot."

"And useful things too," Three scoffs, "like how to shovel horse shit."

"I'm learning a little about farming and how to work with Shady."

"What do you mean 'work with Shady'? Your first riding lesson isn't for a couple of days yet."

"I'm learning how to take proper care of her. You know, like how to clean her stall, what and how much to feed her, and how to brush her coat."

Just talking about Shady is calming. My emotions are slowly settling down. When I'm with her, to some degree at least, my other troubles seem to fade. I relax and lean back in my chair with my feet stretched out in front of me.

"Do you like the horse?"

"Yes. Shady and I are becoming good friends."

"Shady hates your guts," Three says. "Just wait. She'll be the death of you."

"The two of you met just a little while ago."

"Yes, but Shady likes what I do for her and she doesn't go berserk like Mom when I stop to defend my powers or adjust the balance of good and evil."

"Do you mean when you stop to tap your toes and the like?"

"Yes."

"How do those on the farm respond when you must take action, you know, to restore the balance of good and evil?"

"Although Guy watches me closely, none of them say anything about it."

"They think you're crazy," Three says.

"Do you think they understand what you're doing?"

"No, they haven't asked about it and I haven't tried to explain."

"So they haven't said anything. But do they react in other ways?"

"They seem to have accepted that what I do is necessary."

"They're afraid to do or say anything that will set you off," Two says.

"Does this help?"

"It helps a lot."

"So, you feel more at ease on the farm?"

"Yes. I like being around Shady. And Derris, Uncle Guy and Aunt Eva's son, who is my age, and I work together all the time and are becoming friends. He has questions about the city and I have questions about farming."

"What about your uncle Guy?"

"Sometimes he makes me nervous. There's something about the way he watches me. I know mother is afraid of him because he is an atheist."

Dr. Levy frowns.

"Oh, don't get me wrong. Even though Guy is a bit strange, it's still better for me on the farm."

"That's what I was hoping," Dr. Levy says with satisfaction. "I want to know more about Guy, Eva and Derris, but let's talk for a little bit now about last Sunday in church."

I sit up straight, tightly gripping the arms of my chair.

"Talking about this makes you anxious, doesn't it?"

"Yes," my voice is a whisper. "Sunday morning was horrible and Sunday night wasn't much fun either."

Tell me about it," Dr. Levy says."

For the next forty-five minutes, Dr. Levy and I talk about what happened to me in church the previous Sunday.

"So, to conclude, the congregation is trying to drive you out of the church," Dr. Levy says. "Satan says they are doing so because God has commanded them, but you know that it is actually Satan and his demons that are responsible. They have fooled the congregation."

"Yes! The members of the church don't know anything about my mission."

"And you've explained all this to your mother?" Dr. Levy asks.

"I've tried, but I don't think she understands."

I squirm in my chair.

"Are you aware your mother has become even more concerned about you lately?"

"*And well she should,*" Three says.

"She's clearly mad at me."

"She didn't tell me about being angry with you. She sounded worried."

"She's angry. Trust me. She thinks that I'm acting up."

"What do you mean?"

"She thinks I'm acting out because we changed churches. She's going to make me go to Holy Cross whether I like it or not."

"So she still thinks it's all a matter of discipline?" Dr. Levy asks.

"Yes."

"Does she understand what the church members did to you?"

"She doesn't believe I'm being assaulted and she doesn't believe the parishioners' voices are entering my mind."

"Way back at the beginning, before you went into the hospital, wasn't Satan putting his thoughts directly into your mind?"

I feel the chill that now accompanies even the mention of Satan.

"Yes, but that is different."

"How is it different?"

"Satan is putting blasphemous thoughts into my mind using my own thinking voice so that God will think the thoughts are mine and condemn me."

I grimace as bile rises in my throat.

"I know this is hard for you, but what were the parishioners doing?"

"The parishioners attacked me with their thoughts using their own voices. Their commands were entering my mind from outside. My demons are inside my mind."

"It must be chaotic."

"It's so hard at times. More and more, I'm having trouble separating what others are saying from my own thoughts."

"He's becoming more and more confused," Three agrees. "He can't tell his friends from his enemies."

"How do the parishioners get into your mind?"

"Satan's demons have been letting them in. The members of the church enter my mind, give their commands, wait for me to respond, and then leave."

All of a sudden it strikes me. God has given me the power to control the thoughts and actions of others by inserting my own thoughts into their minds, like I did with George in the hospital. And now Satan has given these same powers to the parishioners in his attempt to control my mind.

"Are you sure it isn't the other way around?" One asks. "Are you certain it is God that gave you your powers? Have you considered the possibility these powers might be a gift from our Master?"

I shudder violently.

"You're distorting the facts!"

"Are we?"

What if my demons are right? How will I ever know?

"If Satan is now recruiting the congregation, would you say that he's escalating his battle with you?" Dr. Levy asks.

"Yes," I gasp. "My battle with Satan is getting more and more difficult. It's now much more complicated and confusing. Sometimes I can't keep track of who is doing what."

Dr. Levy leans forward, looking directly into my eyes.

"What do you mean?"

"I'm no longer sure what God is doing and what Satan is doing."

Dr. Levy turns in his chair to look out the window, then suddenly turns back to face me.

"What do you think of spending your weekends at your uncle Guy's?"

"It might be the only thing that saves me. I'm afraid to go back to church, afraid of what might happen."

"I've suggested to your mother that it might be a good idea," Dr. Levy continues.

"I know. She's not buying it. She thinks I need discipline."

"So you think she's going to resist?"

"She's already made up her mind. She says I can go to Guy's during the week, but after I come in to see you on Friday morning, I have to stay home for the weekend and go to church."

I tremble at the thought of attending another church service.

***"Your mother may kill you before Shady has a chance,"
Three says.***

Dr. Levy takes a long drink of coffee from his lopsided

mug and remains silent for a moment, deep in thought.

"How do *you* feel about not attending church?"

"God's instructed us all to gather together to worship Him and pray. It's part of my responsibility as a Christian."

"But how do you *feel* about it?"

"The church has always been my refuge."

"What do you mean?"

"I've always felt close to God in church."

"And how do you feel now?"

"Now I think attending church is dangerous for me."

Dr. Levy waits as though he knows there is more to come.

Sitting in silence, I'm suddenly overcome by the agony that seems to fill my days. I burst into tears.

Dr. Levy waits patiently.

My tears eventually stop flowing and I wipe my eyes with the back of my hand.

"The members of the church have abandoned me to Satan to save themselves. They won't help me. They've betrayed me. I've got to get away from the Holy Cross congregation."

Tears run freely down my checks again.

"Don't give up on your church just yet," Dr. Levy says. "Perhaps in time the parishioners will…"

"Don't you see? I can't trust them. I don't know if they're on God's side or Satan's."

"Well, as I was saying…"

"No! God is testing me. He's preparing me to go it alone. I have to figure out for myself what is and what isn't true. I must be stronger than the parishioners, as well as Satan and his demons. There is so much I don't understand."

I slump in my chair. This is going to be much harder than I thought.

"Robin," Dr. Levy says softly, "we'll figure all this out. It will be hard work and probably take us awhile, but I promise you things will get better. Do you think you're up to the task?"

"I…I suppose…What choice do I have?"

"Good. Then, we'll work on this together."

Dr. Levy starts to write in my file, but abruptly stops. Setting his pen down, he takes his glasses off and puts them on his desk, then rubs his eyes with his fists.

"Dr. Levy?"

"Yes."

"If I'm not accepted at church, where do I belong?"

"What about the farm?"

"I can't hide there forever. I have a mission from God that must be completed. Besides, I'll never make a good farmer. What am I supposed to do?"

"All in good time," Dr. Levy remarks. "All in good time."

16

"I don't think it's a good idea for him to be working with knives," Mother warns, looking directly at me. "He was pretty shaky after talking to Dr. Levy this morning. All he'll tell me is that they talked about what happened in church last Sunday."

"For crying out loud, Lora," Father replies. "He's fourteen years old."

"Just make sure he stays in the back room."

That's what Mother's really worried about. She doesn't want customers to see me. She's ashamed of me.

"I can't say that I blame her," Three agrees. "Your behavior is becoming more and more bizarre. You lost it in church. But then, most of the parishioners lost it in that church long before you."

"Come on, son, we'll get you started. You've got some hay and grain to buy for the winter. This'll be a good way to learn a trade and earn the money you'll need too."

"This ought to be interesting." Three taunts me. "He

can't do anything without some sort of ritual. His mother is probably right. He's going to cut off a finger."

Dad leads me down the stairs from the office and, disregarding mother's request, takes me out into the store itself, past the dairy display cases, and then back into the produce preparation room. I tiptoe and tap my toes all the way, drawing the stares of several customers.

"Hi, Bob," Frank says.

He turns to me.

"Robin, I hear you got yourself a horse."

"Yeah, and she's a cattle horse!"

"Trained to cut and rope, right?"

"And she's been shown in rodeos for bravery!"

"Sounds like a fine animal, much fancier than the old draft horses on my mother's farm."

"Get real," Three utters. "They're all dumb farm animals."

"You use draft horses?'

"My son uses a tractor. With all the produce he grows, horses would be too slow in this day and age. I help him whenever I can. Still, now and again I like to get the horses out on weekends. It reminds me of my father and the old days."

"Draft horses are a lot bigger than cattle horses."

Short, slight and wiry, Frank doesn't look big enough to handle draft horses despite his heavily muscled arms and calloused hands. I know he spends every Sunday from sunrise to sunset laboring in his son's fields.

Dad once told me Frank is the only true "Calamity Jane" he's ever met, explaining that nothing, absolutely nothing, ever works out for him. Everything he tries fails and puts him deeper into debt. He can't even get a used car that runs for long. Although our trials are different, I recognize in his eyes the hard determination to prevail that I now feel.

"Have you ridden her yet?" Frank asks.

"The dumb horse will be the death of you," Three continues.

"Her name is Shady and she's not a dumb farm animal. She's a cattle horse."

"I'm going to get my first lesson on Sunday. Dad's going with me."

"Bob, I didn't know that you ride."

Father clears his throat.

"Frank, I want you to teach Robin how to prepare produce for sale."

"Sure enough, Bob. Anything you say."

"And don't give him any special treatment. He's just another trainee."

"Yes, sir. No special treatment."

"Now, Robin, you listen to everything Frank tells you. He's the best produce man in the business. You can learn a lot from him."

Dad turns and leaves.

"Come on in," Frank says. "We'll start you off trimming and bagging lettuce. Our display's getting low and it's as good a place as any to start."

The produce preparation room is designed for easy cleanup. The sunken cement floor, with a large drain in the middle, is covered with wooden flats. These are picked up at the end of the day and the entire floor is hosed clean. The boards are evenly spaced with gaps separating each, creating a minefield of wide cracks.

The cracks are so big. I hesitate.

"Come on in," Frank repeats. "I won't bite."

"I can't step on the cracks."

"What did I tell you?" Three gloats. "He's in trouble already."

"Is that why you were tiptoeing down the aisle in the store just now?"

"Yes, sir."

"What happens when you step on a crack?"

"I lose some of my special powers."

"Your special powers didn't work well for you in church," Two reminds me. "You couldn't even control the minds of God's nasty little flock. Are you sure these powers aren't just a figment of your imagination?"

"You were blocking my thought transmissions in church. You stopped me from communicating with the congregation."

"You couldn't influence the thinking of the parishioners because you don't have any special powers. And even if you did,

God would have blocked your efforts anyway."

"That's not true. My mission's from God."

"Then why didn't he help you?"

Why doesn't God help me? What am I doing wrong?

Frank smiles.

"I think I understand," he says. "I've been falling between cracks of one sort or another all my life and don't like them much either. Tell you what, we're not going to tell your father about this, but I'm going to put down a rubber mat to cover the cracks for you. Do you think that will help?"

"Yes, sir. Thank you."

"Good. You'll be working with knives and I don't want you to trip and cut off a finger."

Frank began to laugh, but stopped short when I didn't.

"Frank will soon discover that nothing is sufficient to make this misfit functional," Two scoffs.

"I do what God requires of me."

"He's not only dysfunctional, but delusional as well," Two remarks.

I put my hands over my ears and sway with the confusion that still plagues me. Although talking with Dr. Levy had helped, I haven't figured out precisely what happened to me in church last Sunday.

Frank doesn't say anything, but carefully lays a black rubber mat across the boards and the spaces between them in the area in front of the lettuce bagging machine where I'm going to work.

"Voilà," Frank exclaims, "no cracks."

"Thank you."

"Think nothing of it, kiddo. Now, let's get you started."

I carefully tiptoe across the flats on the floor to the safety of the mat.

Frank demonstrates how to properly trim and bag a head of lettuce.

"Now, you need to trim and bag three boxes. That's seventy-two heads of lettuce. When you're done with this first box, you can get a couple more out of the cooler. Let's see how fast you can get that done."

"Yes, sir."

"I'm going out front to straighten the display stands."

Frank leaves the room. I know he can't possibly understand my mission or what it requires of me, but he seems to accept my needs at face value. Eager to please, I attack the first box of lettuce with a vengeance.

It takes me about twenty minutes to trim and bag the first twenty-four heads of lettuce.

I look out through the window overlooking the produce department and into the front of the store where I can see Frank talking to an elderly couple. They burst into laughter.

Are they laughing at me? Is he telling them about my difficulty with cracks? Do they think my defenses are funny?

I tiptoe nervously across the flats, enter the cooler, and

retrieve another box of untrimmed lettuce. It's much heavier than I expect. Slowly and carefully I tiptoe back towards the safety of my black mat, but with the box in my arms I can't see my feet. Watching the flooring off to my side, I try desperately to avoid the wide cracks in the flats, testing my footing with each step. Halfway across the room my right toe catches in one of the cracks and I trip. Losing my grip, the box drops to the floor with a loud thud. Pitching forward, I land on top of the box, knocking the wind out of me.

Sprawled across the box, I gasp for air.

"Are you okay?"

I look up expecting to see Frank, but it's Father. He's seen everything.

"Yes," I say.

Suddenly it all seems so ridiculous. I can't help it and I start to laugh, knowing if I didn't, I would cry. Dad sits down on the floor near the lettuce bagging machine and begins to laugh with me.

"Take her halter and hold her steady," Uncle Ray calls from the center of the small corral.

Out of the corner of my eye, I can see Dad, Guy and Derris watching me closely from their perch on the top rail of the corral fence. Jon, Ray's nine-year-old son, runs out of the farmhouse and joins the men on the fence. Jon is five years younger than Derris and me. Uncle Ray has just bought a mare for him. He too is boarding his horse, Ribbon, on Guy's farm. Oddly, Ribbon is bigger than Shady and Derris' horse, Smoky. I think Jon is afraid of her.

"This ought to be good," Derris says.

My mouth is so dry I can barely swallow, but this time it isn't from my medication. Learning to care for Shady is one thing, but riding her for the first time is entirely different.

"You're nuts to get mixed up in this cowboy stuff," Three scolds. "It's dangerous, dirty, and make-believe anyway. You're just stalling for time. "

"Oh, it's okay for you to make snide remarks, but not me. Is that it?"

"The sniveling little brat needs to learn a little respect," Three complains.

"Robin?"

Ray is clearly puzzled by the delay in my response.

Taking an even number of steps to preserve symmetry, I approach Shady and take her halter.

Shady stamps her hooves on the hard-packed earth, turning her head to look at me. Oddly, her huge, dark brown eyes reveal a hint of fear.

What's she afraid of? She's twice my size.

I remember Henderson's comment about Shady being "bottle broken." What did he mean? Has she been mistreated?

Shady shivers and dances around as Ray places my saddle blanket on her back.

"She's a little skittish," Ray observes.

"So am I."

"Don't let her frighten you. Horses can smell fear and will take advantage, so you can't let on."

"If what your uncle Ray says is true, you're in big trouble," Three warns.

I rub one sweaty hand down the side of my new jeans as I hold Shady's halter in the other. I turn to look at Dad. He seems unconcerned.

I take a tighter grip.

Standing erect, carefully distributing my weight equally between my right and left feet to preserve a balance of good and evil, I pretend to know what I'm doing. I try my best to look confident, like a real cowpoke. Sweat forms on the inner band of the white, straw cowboy hat Dad surprised me with that morning.

Ray turns around, bends down, and grabs my saddle at both ends. Just as he's straightening up, Shady rears and shies away. I'm still holding her halter tightly in my right hand. As she rises high up on her hind legs, she lifts me off the ground. As she turns sharply away from the saddle and starts to run toward the other side of the corral, she tosses me aside. With my arms flailing, I land on my butt in a fresh pile of horse shit.

Derris slaps his thighs and doubles over with laughter, falling off his perch on the fence.

Two and Three also begin laughing.

I'm glad everyone finds this so funny. I wonder if anyone was laughing at Derris when he was learning to ride.

Dad, Ray and Guy struggle to keep from laughing, while Jon looks terrified.

"We told you this cowboy stuff is all make-believe, not to mention dangerous," Three insists. "You'd better focus on reality. Our Leader is your only hope."

"The horse shit isn't make-believe. It stinks!"

More important than the pungent odor is the disruption in the balance of good and evil resulting from my being tossed.

"I told you to hold her," Ray says, stifling laughter.

"I did."

Climbing to my feet, I stamp my right foot three times. Out of the corner of my eye, I see Guy watching me intently, an odd look on his face. I know Guy is an atheist. He's said nothing all week about my efforts to maintain the balance of good and evil, so I don't know whether or not he's working with my demons. Satan's cohorts are everywhere.

I start wiping off the disgusting mess that clings to the seat of my jeans.

"Hey, Roy Rogers," Three scoffs, "How do you plan to get the horse shit off your hands?"

"Sometimes it's better to let go of the halter," Guy says, then bursts into laughter.

Looking guilty, he quickly covers his mouth with a calloused hand. Dad and Ray are no longer trying to hide their laughter.

Embarrassed, I stare at my feet.

Guy climbs down off the fence and offers me a gigantic red, paisley handkerchief, the kind all farmers seem to have.

"Here, clean yourself up. We don't want you to mess up your saddle."

Is it possible that Guy is working with Satan's demons? I must protect myself.

Reluctantly, I take Guy's handkerchief. Despite this

contact, I feel no loss of my powers.

Does this mean Guy's not dangerous?

After cleaning the seat of my pants and my hands, I try to return the handkerchief. Guy holds up his hands to keep me at bay.

"Oh, you can keep it," Guy says. Everyone breaks into laughter, even Jon. My face and neck turn red. I'm not feeling like a cowpoke.

"Don't worry about it, Robin," Uncle Ray sympathizes. "It's happened to all of us at least once. If you're a good cowpoke, you'll laugh it off, but never let it happen again."

Do I belong here? Can I become a cowboy?

"We've been trying to tell you that this is not part of your destiny," One joins in. "You're out of place here."

"You don't approve of the farm? Do you think I should stay home and go to church?"

"Of course not," One replies.

But where do I belong? Our church isn't a refuge for me anymore. I'm not a cowboy either. Has God abandoned me as my demons are suggesting?

"You are our Master's protégé," One insists. "Count your blessings."

"I think I'll just stay on the farm, thank you."

"What's all this nonsense about Guy?" Two asks.

"I think Guy may be one of your agents."

"That's ridiculous," Three says.

My demons are defending Guy. That's not a good sign. I must be careful of him!

"Please!" Three says. "Guy's a farmer. Do you think we need his help?"

Are my demons trying to hide something? There's no refuge for me, not in church and not here. But Derris, Jon, Guy and Eva, Guy's wife, are the only ones I'll have to deal with on the farm. That's better than a whole congregation of assailants. I'm staying on the farm.

"Haven't you been listening?" Three sneers. "We've been telling you who you are and who you are to become. The fact that we're spending all this time with you should give you a clue. You're one of us."

Why isn't God helping me? How can I possibly succeed at my mission if God doesn't protect me? It's never occurred to me until this moment that I might fail to complete my mission. Does the fact that I can't keep my demons out mean I'm one of them?

"Bingo," Three agrees. "I think he's beginning to get the message."

This can't be.

"You're not paying attention," Dad says. "You've got to listen up if you expect to learn to ride."

"Tell him you're not interested in the horse or in walking around in shoes with high heels," Three interjects.

I laugh at Three's remark.

Dad looks hurt, as if he thinks I'm mocking him.

Not knowing what to say, I look away.

"Forget about it," Derris says. "It won't be the last time. If it isn't road apples, it'll be cow patties. And trust me, the horse shit is better."

Everyone bursts into laughter.

"Sounds like you're going to be filthy and stinky all the time," Three chuckles. "Dr. Levy picked a real winner of a sport."

"Robin?" It's Uncle Ray.

"What?"

"Are you ready to get back to saddling Shady?"

Derris chases Shady into a corner of the corral, grabs her halter, and leads her back to me. Like his father, he looks like a farmer. He has curly hair and is two inches shorter than me. He's strong from working the farm. He's also smart and practical. His cowboy boots and fancy western shirt are new, but his jeans are tattered and his straw cowboy hat is frayed.

"Let's give it another try," Uncle Ray says.

Saddling Shady goes off without a hitch the second time. Ray shows me how to locate the saddle and fasten the cinches.

On the other hand, putting on Shady's bridle is a little frightening. She has big teeth and I'm in no mood to be bitten after having been tossed, but the job is soon done.

"I think I'd better loosen her up first," Ray says.

Passing the reins on either side of Shady's neck, he takes them into his left hand.

"You always mount a horse from the left side."

"Why?"

Although I still have some hope of becoming a cowboy, of finding refuge here, always mounting from the left is troubling. I'll have to find a way to compensate for the imbalance this will create.

"Because that's what horses are trained to expect," Ray replies.

Ray takes hold of the saddle horn with his left hand, easily managing the reins with this same hand. I expect him to put his left foot into the stirrup and pull himself up like Gene Autry and all the other movie cowboys. But Ray turns to face in the opposite direction from Shady. He throws his right leg up and over Shady's back, swinging up into the saddle in a single motion. I watch with admiration.

"You should always swing into the saddle like that," Guy says.

"Why?" I challenge.

Is there a hidden purpose in Guy's comment? Is he trying to trick me into disrupting the balance of good and evil?

Guy stands silently, staring at me for a minute before speaking.

"If the horse shies, you won't end up getting dragged off with your foot stuck in the stirrup. It's good horsemanship."

This seems like an innocent comment, but always swinging into the saddle from the left side is certain to disturb the balance of good and evil.

Derris opens the corral gate.

Ray loosens the reins and squeezes Shady around the

middle with his legs. She jumps into a quick trot, but Ray reins her back into a walk.

"She's going to be fast," Ray says, as he rides in a large circle in the open area between the farmhouse, the corral, and the unused milking barn.

"How can you tell when you're just walking her?" Father asks.

"When you say a horse is fast, you mean she's always eager to run and has to be held back," Ray calls back over his shoulder. "Robin will need a strong bit to hold her. I also see why she was shown for bravery. She's got a lot of spirit, even for a top-notch working horse."

"Do you think Robin can handle her?" Guy asks as if I wasn't there.

"Old man Henderson thought we were crazy to buy her for Robin," Ray remarks, "that he's too young. But then he doesn't know Robin. I think Shady and he will make a good match. Robin's got as much spirit as Shady. He already fishes like a man. He'll be just fine."

My chest swells.

"Let's just be sure we get the right bit," my dad says, clearly concerned.

"Don't get swell-headed," Three warns. "This huge beast is going to be running away with you all the time. You'll fall and break your back. And when you're riding around in a wheelchair, they'll talk about how much spirit you have. Have we forgotten about common sense?"

Ray takes Shady at a cantor up the driveway to the main road and back.

"She handles beautifully!" Ray exclaims. "She responds well to commands. Her trot is pretty rough, but her cantor is as smooth as glass."

I think she looks magnificent, sleek and powerful. This is my horse. Maybe I can become a cowboy.

Ray takes both feet out of the stirrups and swings out of the saddle.

"Now, Robin, it's your turn.".

My stomach knots up, leaving me queasy. I try not to let it show.

Ray hands me the reins. I pass the reins on either side of Shady's neck and take them in my left hand, just as Uncle Ray did. Grasping the saddle horn, the right-hand rein slips out of my hand. I gather up the loose rein and try again. The same thing happens.

"You'll never get this right," Two taunts me. "Give it up!"

"Here, let me show you how to hold the reins," Uncle Ray offers.

He demonstrates how to hold the reins in my hand.

"This way you can adjust the length of the reins independently and can also grab other things with your left hand, like the saddle horn or a rope."

Fumbling, I finally get the reins right. Grabbing the saddle horn with my left hand, I turn to face the direction opposite Shady. Then I try to throw my right leg up and over her back.

What I actually do is kick Shady hard in the hindquarters and fall flat on my back, dropping the reins. Startled, Shady sidesteps and then trots away, her reins dragging on the ground on either side.

I make no effort to get up.

"Good show," Three jeers. "You're making a fool of yourself."

Derris and Guy are laughing again. Ray looks down at me lying on my back. Dad rushes over to my side.

"Are you all right?"

I start to laugh.

"He's all right," Ray says.

Looking at Jon from where I am lying, I can see that he's terrified and close to tears. His turn is next.

"Do you want to do this horse stuff?" Three interjects. "It's a lot of monkey business just to get on the wild beast. Don't be a fool."

"We'll see who the fool is once I get this down pat. I'll be able to ride anywhere."

God, why aren't you helping me?

Suddenly the subtle presence of my guardian angel sends a rush of confidence and composure through me.

"He can learn to mount later," Guy says. "Let's just get him on the horse."

Dad extends a hand and pulls me to my feet.

I stamp my right foot five times.

Dad and Ray simply wait. Guy looks disturbed.

Guy doesn't like it when I adjust the balance of good and

evil. Is he involved with Satan? This could be a serious problem.

"We've been telling you, this Guy is not one of us," Two mutters.

This heightens my concern.

I've got to keep my eye on Guy all the time.

Derris brings Shady back.

"Grab the reins and the horn again," Ray instructs. "I'll give you a hand up."

Guy takes hold of the bridle to make sure Shady can't dance away.

Ray cups his hands together, his interwoven fingers creating a stepping stool. I put my left boot into his hands and swing up into the saddle.

Before doing anything else, I put my boots into the stirrups and stand in the saddle, putting all my weight on my right foot and stirrup just long enough to compensate for having mounted Shady from the left side. Now I'm sitting pretty.

Maybe I'm beginning to get the hang of this.

Then Guy lets go of the bridle.

Shady begins to buck wildly. Dropping the reins, I grab the saddle horn with both hands and hang on for dear life. My butt is up off the saddle and then back down hard each time Shady arches her back, leaps into the air, and then comes down. I think I'm going to split in two.

Guy moves in quickly to grab the loose reins, bringing Shady back under control.

"You don't want to drop the reins like that," he tells me. "You can't control a horse without reins."

I struggle to get my breath.

Can I control Guy? Will I need to use some of my special powers on him?

"But Shady didn't throw him," Derris says with surprise, even respect.

"What do you think, Guy?" Ray asks.

"He needs some learning, but he's got guts. I think we've got the makings of a damn good cowpoke here," Guy replies. A broad smile lights up his face.

Guy and I return Shady to her stall. He shows me where and how to store Shady's saddle and bridal, and how to rub her down after a workout. I give her a handful of oats as a reward for the day. Then Guy and I return to the farmhouse where the others are waiting.

Aunt Eva has cooked a farmer's dinner of fried chicken, ham, fresh green beans, carrots, mashed potatoes with gravy, and corn bread. We wash it all down with thick, creamy whole milk and top it off with apple pie.

Father plans to leave after dinner, but I'm going to stay on the farm for the week as he has arranged.

"You did good, son," Dad says, as I walk with him to the car. "You're going to master this riding business in no time."

"Can I get a lariat and a Winchester Model 94 like real

cowboys have?"

"We'll get you a rope, but you know how I feel about guns."

"But all cowboys have a scabbard and lever action Winchester 30-30," I insist.

"You like it on the farm, don't you?"

"It's okay."

"Do you realize you don't seem to have as much trouble on the farm as you do at home, especially in church?"

"There aren't so many people around here."

"There's more to it than that, isn't there, son?" Dad asks.

"Yes, I guess there is."

This is the first hint that my father has any idea of what I'm going through.

"Well, for now, I think you're better off out here with Shady."

"Like your father would know," Three says. "You don't belong in either place."

I'll never make a good farmer or a real cowboy. But, being on the farm is clearly better, at least for now.

I'm overcome with homesickness as I watch my father drive away, wondering if in addition to being forced out of the church, I'm going to lose my family.

Smiling and waving goodbye, I already know the answer to my question. Satan has chosen me as a battleground in his war with God. His immediate objective is to separate me in some fashion from all the places where I've always found peace and comfort, and from all those I love and with whom I feel safe. He's trying to cut me out of the herd, where I'm more vulnerable. Win or lose, in the end, I'll never again have the same relationship with my family or the church.

The subtle presence of my guardian angel once again passes over my mind, leaving me with a measure of reassurance and peace. God is comforting me. Yet, I'm only now coming to realize the nature of the sacrifices that His mission will require of me.

17

". . . and let these, Thy gifts to us, be blessed," Father prays, his head bowed and hands folded. As always, we hold a moment of silence for those less fortunate.

"I don't even want to talk about it," Mother exclaims.

"Please pass the scrambled eggs," Carl says.

I don't respond.

Carl tries again.

"Please pass…"

"Wake up, Robin," Mother snaps. "Pass the eggs."

Father reaches across the table, grabs the bowl in front of me and hands it to Carl.

"Take it easy on your brother," Father says. "It didn't work out well for him the last time he attended church."

There's trouble brewing. Why do I always get so anxious? Why do my parents fight over me?

"It didn't work out well for him!" Mother exclaims. "He was acting up. He embarrassed all of us."

"She's never going to get it, is she?" Three asks.

"I don't think he was acting up," Father counters. "Something about the church service terrified him."

I feel detached from the scene, the subject but not a participant. It's as if the discussion would or could not have any effect on me. I'm indifferent.

This must be the effect of the increase in my medication. Dr. Levy is right. In some ways, the higher dose is protecting me from the conflicts that surround me.

"He looked pretty scared to me," Carl says, as he turns to look directly at me. "Did something frighten you or were you just acting up?"

"He just wants to go back to Redeemer," Mother replies. "It's all a ruse. But he's not going to get his way."

I can't stand much more of this.

"Lora," my father says, "I think Robin would be better off spending his weekends on the farm. Guy will welcome him."

"He needs to be in church," Mother insists. "Guy will understand."

"For crying out loud, Lora, he's been in church every Sunday of his entire life and just graduated after six years in the church's parochial school. He's spending the week on the farm. I don't think spending his weekends there, at least for a while, is going to adversely affect his religious education."

"And I think he should be attending the church's youth group meetings on Sunday night too," Mother presses. "He has to make new friends."

"Does she really think these do-gooder kids will be your friends? They'll assault you just like the rest of God's pitiful flock."

"But Derris and Jon are my friends."

"Robin is a different person because of all this," Father says softly.

"And that's why he needs to make new friends," Mother replies. "That's why he needs to attend the church youth group meetings."

"You're right about Robin being a different person," Carl interjects. "Just look at what happened to him in church the last time he went."

"Don't get smart, Carl," Mother snaps.

"He was barely able to make it up the aisle," Carl continues.

"You stay out of this," Mother demands. "This doesn't concern you."

"He may be stupid, but he's still my little brother. And he's not doing well."

"Precisely," Mother exclaims. "He needs my attention and he needs the church."

"Is your mother displaying a touch of guilt over what's happening to you?" Two asks. "She's spent most of her time, not with you, but working in the family store."

"Lora, you haven't seen Robin on the farm," Father replies. "He does much better there."

"It's the congregation," I say.

"What?" Carl asks, trying to encourage me to speak out.

"They're terrified of me. All the parishioners think I'm possessed. No one wants me to attend services."

"We congratulate you," Three says mockingly. "Stand up for yourself. Be firm."

"Robin, that's enough," Mother scolds me. "I won't listen to this nonsense."

"See what I mean about Robin being different," Carl says, smiling. "I rest my case."

"Carl, this isn't funny," Father chides.

"You haven't heard what the parishioners are saying," Carl blurts out.

Mother drops her hands to her sides.

"What are they saying?"

"I've already told you that they all think I'm possessed."

"Tell them that the congregation is trying to drive you insane," Three urges.

"What do you mean by 'possessed?'" Father sounds uneasy.

"They think I'm filled with demons."

"Now you've done it," Two says.

"That's nonsense," Mother replies, her voice laced with fear. "You're imagining things."

"No, Mother. It's true. The congregation assaults me with their thoughts. They think I'm sick," I mutter to myself. "Maybe it'll help if they hear the truth."

"What did you just say?" Carl asks.

"I don't belong in that church. But without the church, I'm no one."

"Here we go again," Mother sighs.

"You are one of us," One declares. "You have finally begun the process of coming home to your own."

"I've never been one of you and never will be!"

"You're flirting with fire," Two warns. "Do you want to end up at Eastern State?"

"Give me patience!" Mother complains, shaking her head.

"Then who am I?" I challenge.

"You're my son," Father says.

"Don't encourage him, Bob," Mother exclaims.

"No one understands me."

"You can't be 'nobody'," Carl mutters.

"Am I still your son?"

"What do you mean?"

"How can I be me, let alone your son, if I can't control my own thoughts?"

"What are you talking about?" Carl asks.

"You'll always be my son," Father replies.

"How can I be your son? Satan has claimed me. He's made his mark. His demons are constantly interfering with my thinking, telling me that I'm becoming one of them. And if I go to church, the congregation does pretty much the same thing except they're terrified of me and don't want anything to do with me."

"This is nonsense!" Mother exclaims. "I won't stand for it. Not in my home."

"Calm down, Lora," Father orders her, as he studies my face.

"Please help me," I plead.

Mother looks away, hiding her tears.

"Help you with what?" Father asks.

"Who am I? I don't want to belong to Satan."

"Well, then it's settled," Father says firmly. "Robin doesn't need this kind of pressure. Dr. Levy is right. He ought to spend his weekends on the farm."

They're all talking about my future as if I'm not even here. To make matters worse, they haven't a clue about my mission or its importance.

"This issue is not settled," Mother counters. "Dr. Levy is supposed to be helping, but Robin's not getting better. If anything, he's getting worse. If the doctors can't help, then God is the only one who can, and for that he needs to be in church."

Does Mother think I'm possessed?

"Besides, Dr. Levy shouldn't be meddling in matters of faith," Mother adds.

"He's not meddling," Father says. "I think he's suggested this because for right now it will be better for Robin."

"If Dr. Levy can't help him, I'm going to find a psychiatrist that can," Mother declares.

Is this a threat? Would she really fire Dr. Levy?

"But Dr. Levy is helping me," I cry.

No one seems to be interested in what I think. It's as if they've already made up their minds.

"What's it going to be?" Father asks in a clipped voice. "Church or a new doctor?"

"Robin needs both," Mother holds firm.

"Robin should stay with Dr. Levy," Father states emphatically, "and we need to follow his advice. We'll take him to church with us today and see how he does. But if he has a problem, beginning next weekend he stays on the farm."

Bursting into tears, Mother jumps up from the table. Knocking her chair over backwards, she runs from the kitchen.

"Someone please help me. I'm alone in your midst and may be lost forever. I don't want to belong to Satan."

As we leave home for Holy Cross, my trembling fingers hover over my chest.

Carl reaches over and pulls my hand away.

"Try not to think about it," he whispers. "I'm sure it will be all right this time if you can just relax."

I know that God will help me when the time is right.

"Church has never been a good idea for anyone." One proclaims, "For you, it is clearly destructive. You must avoid the church if you expect to keep your sanity."

"Are you saying that I must choose between the church and sanity, between God and a future?"

"God has his own agenda," Two says.

"Are you suggesting that God was responsible for the mental illness of my grandfather, my uncle, and my aunt?"

"God can be selfish and cruel." Two whispers as if to suggest this is a closely held secret.

We ride to Holy Cross in silence. I am terrified.

Father pulls into the last free parking spot in the Holy Cross overflow lot. Getting out of the car, I reluctantly follow my family toward the front of the church. My recollection of the last time I was in church, just two weeks ago, hangs over me like a large, black cloud.

Easily managing the cracks in the sidewalk, I dread what I know is coming. I start to tiptoe from tile to tile as we enter the church. Mother sees this and immediately pulls me aside.

"You're in God's house now. You don't need to defend yourself. Say a prayer and straighten up. Act like a good Christian."

That's exactly what I'm trying to do, be a good Christian!

Mother reaches to straighten my tie.

"Look at you." Mother scolds. "Do I have to check on you

like I did when you were five? Your shoes haven't been shined and if I hadn't pressed your suit, you'd be a disgrace."

"Doesn't this tell you something?" Three asks. "This isn't about you. It's all about your mother. She doesn't want to be embarrassed."

By the time we reach the narthex, I have stepped on so many cracks that my toe tapping is slowing me down. As we start up the center aisle, I have to use my special walk.

The entire congregation is now watching me, many of them expressing their disapproval by shaking their heads or holding Bibles out to protect themselves.

Mother's face turns deep red. She storms ahead without me.

Is she just angry, or is she truly ashamed of me?

Father goes ahead with Mother, but Carl trails behind me, allowing me time to negotiate the minefield of cracks.

"What's he doing here again?" someone says. "The boy is possessed."

Why doesn't anyone understand? Why can't they see the truth?

The church members' comments press in on me, making me claustrophobic.

"They don't practice what they preach," Two observes. "Where is the compassion these hypocrites are always talking about? They're quick to judge."

"But you're the ones that started all this."

"Don't try to blame us for what God does with his misguided flock," One says.

"Everyone knows his grandfather and his uncle were either possessed or insane. His aunt is in Eastern State as we speak."

Oh, no! The parishioners are planting their own thoughts in my mind again, just like the last time I was in church.

My breath comes in short gasps. I step on an intersection of cracks. Frantically tapping my toes, distraught over my continuing loss of power, I wonder if I have enough energy left to survive. The temperature seems to rise. I'm suffocating.

"His uncle and aunt had prefrontal lobotomies. His grandfather committed suicide."

My knees weaken. It's getting more and more difficult to avoid cracks.

"His aunt tried to drown her three children"… "the boy is obviously affected"… "his parents should never have brought him into our church."

I stumble yet again. Stepping on a crack, I lose my concentration and more of my special powers.

What they're thinking isn't true. Why would God permit this? He's given me a special mission. How can the voices help me?

"What if he is contagious? Someone get him out of here, now!"

No. They're wrong. I'm wrong. No. I'm right. I'm not contagious.

Stopping, I try to focus my thoughts on the congregation. Maybe I can send them a message if I concentrate. I try to project my thoughts into the minds of the parishioners.

"What you're saying isn't true."

Carl, who's watching the members of the congregation, runs into me from behind.

"The congregation can't hear you," Three taunts me and then breaks into laughter.

"You're blocking my thought transmissions again!"

I focus my entire attention on the parishioners.

"I'm not mentally ill. And I'm not contagious. I'm not possessed. I have a mission from God."

"The boy is just like his aunt. We need to get rid of him. We will not let him contaminate us."

"Just like you thought Mildred was contagious," Two says, "the parishioners think you're contagious. It's the same thing."

Are the members of the church right? Am I mentally ill like Mildred?

"God has the congregation convinced that you are," Two persists.

Do I have to hide from the congregation and from God?

"That's what we've been trying to tell you."

"No! I can't hide from God. I desperately need His help."

"But the congregation speaks for God. He's convinced them you are dangerous."

Once again, I project my thoughts to all those present.

"I'm not a threat to you."

"He is a terrible danger to all of us."

I'm a threat to the con… No. This can't be true. They're trying to control my thoughts again.

Yet again I try.

"I'm not a threat to you."

"He will contaminate us."

I don't know what to believe anymore. Am I truly a danger to them? Or is this church dangerous to me?

I struggle to continue up the center aisle of the church, trying desperately to avoid the cracks, to protect my powers. My mind is a jumble of confusing thoughts.

Reaching our pew near the front of the church, I sit down next to Mother.

The parishioners' verbal assaults continue to penetrate my mind. Their attacks make it difficult to concentrate; their thoughts are becoming my own. It's impossible to sit still.

"He is insane. Satan has him. Why is he here? What does he want?"

"No! I'm not insane! I'm doing God's work."

I try to convince myself that I'm not in danger.

The liturgy starts with its pounding rhythms. The congregation stands up, but I can't. I huddle in place, shaking with chills and sweating, as if I were running a high fever.

Mother grabs my arm and tries to pull me up into a standing position.

Pastor Heines chants and the congregation replies. Like the previous service I had attended, the rhythmic singing thumps like great drum rolls in my ears. The liturgy is followed by a hymn.

"Onward Christian soldiers…"

I remain seated, desperately trying to block out everything going on around me.

Why is God allowing these assaults?

"He's jealous of our Master," One says.

I close my eyes. Putting my hands over my ears, I begin to rock back and forth.

"Just look at him. He's starting another pagan ritual"… "he's deranged…"

Now the parishioners are talking to each other out loud. They no longer care who hears them, but I am only hearing bits and pieces of what they are saying.

"The rumors are right"…"whole family is riddled with insanity"…"It's true that his grandfather…," someone behind me says.

"Listen to us!" Someone across the aisle responds. "You are the devil's seed. You must leave God's house now! You have betrayed God. You let Satan's demons in and you will suffer the consequences."

"I have not betrayed God. I can't keep Satan's demons out, but they don't control me," I reply.

Pastor Heines begins his sermon in what sounds like a foreign language. Not understanding, I have no alternative but to counter every word with an unspoken denial.

The congregation's accusations engulf me like a blizzard. I can't escape them.

My skin is like dry ice, freezing and inflamed at the same time. My chest feels brittle, like some giant scab. I think it might crack and break away at any moment and provide Satan with passage into my heart where he would possess me. I rock back and forth in my seat banging my head on the back of the pew in front of me in an effort to distract myself and to ease the pain.

"Robin!" Mother whispers. "Stop it."

I can feel the protective shield provided by my medication begin to crumble.

I feel as if I'm entirely alone. I'm floating in a sea of uncertainty and foreboding, trying to keep my head above despair.

I feel myself sinking in exhaustion. Dr. Levy's medication is failing.

Mother tries unsuccessfully to force me to stand up with the congregation and sing.

Why is God allowing this?

I'm vaguely aware that the congregation stops singing, sits down, and starts harassing me again. Pastor Heines begins the Gospel reading.

***"God is done with you,"* Three says.**

"No!"

"You are corrupt."

Staring directly at me with a stern expression on his face, Pastor Heines reads from the gospel of Mark. "For Jesus had said to them, 'Come out of this man, you evil spirits.' Then Jesus asked the man, 'What is your name?' 'My name is Legion,' he replied, 'for we are many.'"

Pastor Heines is directing this reading specifically at me. He's referring to Satan and to One, Two, and Three. How does he know? Can't he see that I never invited them in, that they are assaulting me, that I am locked in an epic battle with Satan and his minions and that I need his help and the help of his church?

"We're not at war," One says. "Don't you see that you are becoming one of us, that you're in transition, that you're in the process of coming home?"

"No, I belong to God. He will protect me."

"You have been mine since you were conceived."

Oh, my God, it's Satan again.

"God please help me."

"Your soul has been mine since the beginning of time," Satan continues. "You can't escape. This is my blessing. It's your destiny."

"Never!"

Pastor Heines finally begins his sermon. He's staring straight at me, his words clearly directed at me.

"We must be vigilant. Satan is everywhere. His demons are among us. We must be…"

I can't allow Satan, One, Two, or Three, or any of the parishioners in...

Suddenly I feel Satan pressing against my chest, once again trying to force his way into my heart. I begin to dig at my chest to deny him access. I feel the scab there break.

Pastor Heines continues with his sermon in the background, time slipping by.

My chest is soon bleeding and skin is collecting under my fingernails. Seeing this, Mother frantically tries to stop me. She becomes more and more distressed as the bloodstain on my white dress shirt grows larger.

"In closing, we must remain vigilant," Pastor Heines declares.

Weeping, I fall to the floor, hitting my head on the pew in front of me. I curl up into a ball.

"Robin, are you all right?" Mother says, her voice filled with panic and remorse.

I pull myself up, first onto the pew and then into a standing position. I turn to face the congregation.

"You will never drive me out of God's house," I shout. "I'm not insane and God has not renounced me. I have a sacred mission from God and I won't permit you to interfere!"

The entire congregation is staring at me with their mouths wide open. The bloodstain on my shirt is clearly apparent.

I feel sweat dripping from my forehead and running down my face. Shaking violently from the chill of the evil surrounding me, I'm in danger of falling...

Then it happens, silently, painlessly, without warning. My surroundings slowly fade to grey. Nothing moves. Everything seems suspended in time.

I again sense the presence of my guardian angel.

"What is your name?" I ask.

I feel my mind gently separate into an inner portion and an outer portion. My newly formed inner mind, like the yolk buried deep in the white of a boiled egg, is now completely encased by what remains as my outer mind.

Who has done this?

"I have enabled us to work together, to consult each other, to collaborate."

This thought is clearly being planted directly into my mind, but it's not in my own thinking voice like the thoughts that Satan puts into my mind.

"Who are you? Are you my guardian angel?"

Could this be one of Satan's tricks?

"I'm a function of your inner mind," the new voice continues.

"What does that mean?" I ask.

"I'm a part of you and you are a part of me, we are one and the same."

"Why is this happening to me?"

"I am to preserve us."

"But who are you?"

"I'll call myself by our middle name, I will be 'Hugh'."

What if this is just another one of Satan's tricks?

I suddenly realize that Satan, his demons, and all the other voices that have constantly plagued me are now completely silent.

"Where have all my voices gone?" I ask Hugh.

"I've blocked them out for the time being," Hugh replies.

"Out…What do you mean? Where are we?"

"We are in a safe place. We are within our inner mind. God is with us."

18

"He seems to be fine now, Pastor Heines," Father says softly.

"All the other parishioners have left," Heines replies. "Are you sure you don't want me to call an ambulance?"

"I don't think that'll be necessary," Mother interjects. "We'll just take him home where he can get some rest."

Father leads me out of the church and gets me settled in the car. Carl crowds into a corner so that I can lie down on the back seat. We start for home.

"How can I be sure you're not one of Satan's tricks?" I ask Hugh.

"How much assurance do you need?" One demands. "We've explained and demonstrated time and again, we are not a trick. Our Leader has your best interests in mind."

"I'm not talking to you."

"Hugh, I thought you'd blocked out all the voices that harass me."

"You seem to have recovered a bit," Hugh replies, "so I didn't think it was necessary any longer."

"Am I still in our inner mind with you?"

"Yes," Hugh confirms, "and while you're here, you'll be protected from all your voices. You can hear them well enough, but they can't harm you."

"Can I just stay here forever?"

"No. I can only let you stay here until you've regained your strength."

"Who the hell are you talking to?" Two demands.

I realize with a start that Satan's demons cannot hear the thoughts Hugh is planting in my mind.

"I'm not sure."

"I don't think we should take Robin out to the farm today," Mother declares.

"We shouldn't have taken him to church," Father replies. "I'm not sure what just happened. But whatever it was, I think he needs to see Dr. Levy as soon as possible. And this time we're going to follow the doctor's advice."

"Well, if you don't know who you're talking to, who does?" Three complains.

"Is Hugh one of you?"

"Who the hell is Hugh?" Three asks. His frustration is apparent.

"I'm talking to Hugh, but I'm not entirely sure who he is," I stammer.

"Forget about this Hugh, whoever he might be," Satan interjects, his voice dripping with malevolence. *"You are now and always have been one of mine. You'll not escape me this easily."*

God help me. Satan is back, but obviously he, just like his demons, can't hear Hugh either.

"Robin, there is a way that you and I can communicate and no one will be able to eavesdrop," Hugh says. "I think we ought to do this."

"How can we do that?"

"How can we do what?" Satan demands.

"Just think in the voice in which you now hear me," Hugh explains.

"Do you mean this voice?"

"Yes! Hugh says. "With this voice we can think together and no one can hear our thoughts."

"I'll call Dr. Levy first thing in the morning," Mother agrees.

"I don't know any more than you do," Hugh replies. "But like you, I suspect Satan's claims that he owns you are just wishful thinking. I'm here, at least in part, to ensure that his desires are not realized."

"Are you my guardian angel?" I ask.

"I'm not an angel." Hugh replies. "As I explained before, I am a part of you and you are a part of me. We are one and the same."

"How can that be? If we are one and the same, wouldn't I know this already, just like you do?"

"Trust me. It'll all become clear to you in time," Hugh replies.

"I'm not sure that I can trust you, let alone believe you."

"Then, let me ask you this," Hugh says. "How do you feel?"

"How do I feel?"

"Yes. How do you feel right now?"

I've been so wrapped up in the mysterious appearance of this Hugh, whoever or whatever he may be, that I haven't noticed that I'm no longer anxious, no burning skin and no molten anxiety beneath it.

"I'm at peace."

"Do you find the voices of our demons disturbing?"

"Not right now."

"That tells you we're together in our inner mind where we're safe from such intrusions. When you're in our inner mind, you can choose to monitor but ignore Satan and all his demons. They can let others into our outer mind, but not our inner mind. This way they'll have no impact on you. Or, with my permission, you can choose to block them out altogether."

Is Hugh a gift from God or a product of my imagination? Is he one of Satan's horrible tricks, or is he essential to the completion of my mission?

"Robin, you are an ingrate," Three scolds. "I think it'd be appropriate for you to thank our Master for his patience and understanding."

"I have never been, and I will not become, one of your Master's minions."

I spend the remainder of Sunday and Monday morning in my room. Hugh allows me to remain within our inner mind. He appears to have gone, but I can sense his continuing presence. I elect to block out all my voices.

Mother brings my meals to me on a tray. No one bothers me. I think they're afraid of precipitating another "incident," as my parents and Carl call it when they think I can't hear them. I wouldn't have responded to anyone in any event. The last thing I want is to hear anyone's voice. With strains of "Don't Fence

Me In" and "Old No. 9," as well as other favorites playing in the background, I bathe in a peaceful, blissful silence. I feel myself gathering strength and confidence, as if much of the power that has been drained from me in recent months is finding its way back home.

Mother calls Dr. Levy first thing Monday morning and arranges for us to meet with him that afternoon.

We arrive early, about 1:45 p.m., and have to wait in the reception area for about twenty minutes before he emerges from his office.

"If you don't mind waiting, Mrs. Cunningham," Dr. Levy says, "I'd like to talk to Robin first."

Mother looks a little peeved, but sits down in a leather wing chair near the window to wait.

"How are you this afternoon, Robin?" Dr. Levy asks. "Are you feeling any better? Your mother told me on the phone that things were extremely difficult for you in church yesterday."

Now that I am in Dr. Levy's office and being asked to discuss the events that took place in church the day before, my demons attempt to resume their assaults on me. I decide to no longer block them out completely so I can monitor their efforts, but because I am still at the center of my mind, their comments simply don't bother me.

"Robin, you still haven't told us who you were talking to after church yesterday," Two complains. "I think we have a right to know."

I remain silent.

"It's important for us to know," One pressures me.

Dr. Levy's the only one who might even come close to understanding what's happening to me. It's essential to my mission that I understand the significance of yesterday's events. He's the only one who can help me.

"You'll regret it for the rest of your life if you discuss yesterday's drama with your shrink," Three warns. "Like all other shrinks, he'll betray you in the end."

"Robin, are you all right?" Dr. Levy asks. Although firm, his voice seems muffled.

"I'm okay," I whisper. "Mother was right when she said a lot happened yesterday. Things got pretty bad in church."

"However," Dr. Levy continues, "I understand that by the time you got home from church you were doing okay."

"Yes. I was doing just fine."

"You were not doing 'just fine,'" Two says. "You'd completely withdrawn. You can't realize your destiny if you withdraw. You must stay engaged. We were afraid we had lost you forever."

"How are you feeling now?"

"I truly feel better than I have in a long time."

"Can you tell me what happened during the church service?"

"One, Two, Three, and the parishioners all assaulted me in church."

"That's happened to you before," Dr. Levy observes, "but you handled it well enough. Was there something more?"

"Satan also assaulted me."

"What did he say?"

"He claimed that I've always been his, that I'm turning into one of his demons, and that there's nothing I can do to stop it."

"Do you believe him?" Dr. Levy asks.

"You know I don't."

"Why is your shrink ignoring the fact that you completely withdrew?" Two asks. "This can't be good. Any competent psychiatrist knows that."

"You've dealt with all this before, so what made yesterday so rough?" Dr. Levy presses.

"Pastor Heines was preaching directly at me. He demanded that I keep One, Two, and Three out of my life. He said I wouldn't be saved if I can't do this."

"Did he mention One, Two, and Three by name?" Dr. Levy asks.

"I think so."

"But you're not sure?"

"No, I'm not sure. By that time things were starting to spiral out of control."

"It's not surprising that you can't remember," Dr. Levy volunteers. "You were under a great deal of stress."

"I guess the thing that set me off was the combination of everything all at once. It was the accumulation of all the voices, the liturgy, the pounding music, the sermon, everything!"

"I'm not surprised by what happened," Dr. Levy says. "I'm surprised it hasn't happened to you sooner. It's precisely why I think you need a break from church, that you should spend your weekends on the farm, at least for a while."

"I think that's a good idea."

"I don't believe this," Two says. "Robin's shrink is sanctioning a form of withdrawal. Is that good medical practice?"

"You just don't like the fact that you couldn't, and still can't, influence me when I'm in my inner mind."

"This 'inner mind' is a delusion," One says. "If you're going to realize your destiny, you must stay engaged so that we can prepare you."

"Well," Dr. Levy observes, "after yesterday maybe we'll be able to get you the break you need."

"Good."

"There's something that does surprise me though," Dr. Levy adds.

"What's that?"

"I'm stunned by the fact that by the end of the service you were so calm, and that you're so calm now. I would have expected you to be in anguish. Is there something you're not telling me?"

"Hugh, should I tell Dr. Levy about you and about our inner mind? Should I explain that I'm so calm, even now, precisely because I'm still in our inner mind with you?"

"I think it's probably best if Dr. Levy doesn't know about me just yet," Hugh replies. "Telling him now would probably complicate things a bit too much. The time to explain all this will come soon enough."

"I'm sorry, Dr. Levy, but I can't talk about it."

"We've always been honest with each other," Dr. Levy says, "so, is there a specific reason why you can't talk about it?"

"Because I'm not sure what happened."

"But, Hugh, you know as well as I do that it's essential to the success of my mission that I come to a complete and full understanding of what's happening to me. I need to know who, or what, you are, as well as the part in all this you're going to play."

"All in good time," Hugh replies.

As Mother and I pass through the exit door onto the street in front of Dr. Levy's office building, the piercing sounds of the street strike me like a slap in the face, shaking me violently. The noise penetrates my mind and consciousness like a bullet crashing through my skull. Suddenly, I, Robin, am no longer resident in my inner mind with Hugh. I'm back where I've always been, but it's now far more chaotic than ever.

There are seldom many people on the sidewalks of downtown Spokane, but all those here now are trying to talk over each other. The volume of these conversations, loud to begin with, rises and falls as we approach, pass and then leave individuals behind. Their voices are now crowding into my mind, each jostling with the others, trying to gain a foothold, to obtain my undivided attention. If I can hear them with my ears, they're present in my mind, and their thoughts become my own. I can't keep them out. My outer mind is in utter chaos.

"Hugh, why aren't you protecting me from all these voices, all this confusion? I thought God sent you to protect me."

"You've recovered from the crisis you experienced in church," Hugh replies, "so it was essential that you return to the outside world. Except for emergencies, you must remain in the outside world if we're to defeat Satan and complete our mission. This is where you must engage the forces against us. I'm here to preserve us, but that's not necessarily the same as protecting you."

Hugh's statement seems to contain a subtle and possibly ominous message.

"We warned you, didn't we?" Two asks. "Our Benefactor is putting you on notice by allowing everyone into your mind. Is this how you want to spend the balance of your days? You'll end up in Eastern State for sure, just like your grandfather, uncle, and aunt."

"Remember," Hugh says, "the completion of our mission is our only objective."

I can barely make out Hugh's voice, or even my own, over the clamor of all the others passing by on the street.

"Hugh, what do you mean when you say you're here to preserve us, but not to protect me?"

"In part it means I can intervene in your struggle with Satan and his minions only when you are in extreme danger," Hugh replies. "And even then the number of times I can do this is limited. Otherwise, my interference could alter events significantly enough to destroy our mission. By and large, you must face Satan and his demons alone and head on, and you must prevail."

While the conversations of passersby might seem

irrelevant, the fact that they occur within earshot, penetrating my outer mind and becoming my thoughts, endows them with extraordinary power.

"Hugh, if you're here to help, please do something!"

My skin is ablaze with anxiety, as if I'm being cooked on a rod over a bed of hot coals. The lid of my right eye is twitching.

"We warned you! Our Master is angry with you and now he's taking it out on us as well."

"What else is Satan planning to do to me? I have a right to know."

"He's not just letting random voices into your outer mind," Two explains. "He's shattered the 'shell' that separates your outer mind from everything around it. He's subjecting you to complete exposure to the outside world. You are naked, without protection, except for what we provide."

"God will protect me!"

Mother takes me directly to Guy's. She's still furious over the scene I'd created in church on Sunday, but her face is also clouded with fear. Over the last half hour, she speaks to me only when necessary. She tries to hide it, but I can see all the telltale signs. She is fighting to hold back tears. Whatever Dr. Levy said to her during the five minutes she spent with him in his office has badly shaken her.

As we careen down the highway leading north from Spokane, Mother is preoccupied. When she takes her eyes off the road every so often to look at me, I close mine to avoid eye contact. Concentrating on any one subject for more than a few minutes is hard for me. Even though we are alone in the car, all the voices that have assailed me continue to echo in my mind.

The contrast between my current state and what I had experienced when at the center of my mind with Hugh is alarming in the extreme. I wonder if this is an indication of just how difficult my mission is going to be.

"Hugh, why didn't you warn me that all these voices would have complete access to my outer mind?"

"I had no way of knowing," Hugh replies. "I can't see into the future any more than you can."

"Hugh, is this why the ability to control the passage of time is so important to our mission?"

"I don't know," Hugh replies.

"Are you going to ride all the way out to Guy's without saying a word to me?" Mother complains, taking her eyes off the road to express her displeasure. "Are you trying to give me the silent treatment?"

I don't respond.

"Well?" Mother demands.

"Hugh and I are talking. Please don't interrupt us," I finally respond.

"Hugh?" Mother asks.

"I think Hugh and I might be one."

"What?" Mother asks, looking confused. "What are you talking about? Hugh is just your middle name."

"That's just great," Three complains. "Now he's talking to himself."

I shudder as an ice-cold fear runs up and down my spine.

I can't let anyone or anything stop me. Is God telling me I must complete my mission without help from anyone except Hugh, who claims to be just another part of me? But what if Hugh is lying to me? What if he is one of Satan's underlings? Then listening to his advice could be catastrophic. If my mission fails, the universe will be destroyed.

"You just said that you and Hugh are one," One interjects. "If you take this Hugh's advice, that advice will actually be coming directly from you. So, you'll have no one to blame but yourself for the consequences."

"As promised, you'll always have my help when the chips are down," Hugh says. "And since we're one and the same, God is preparing us, both of us, for battle."

"How do I know I can trust you?"

"Do you trust yourself?" Hugh asks.

"No, I can't trust myself when my mind is playing tricks on itself, when I'm not in control of my own thinking. How do I know you're a part of me?"

"You'll have to trust me, at least for the present," Hugh responds. "This is just the first of many challenges we'll face together."

Voices from all sources, good and bad, past and present, force their way into my mind as Mother and I continue on our way to Guy's. Each only adds to my confusion as they fight for my attention. I feel like I'm in the midst of an enormous electrical storm.

Mother races down the hard-packed earthen road, turns into Guy's long, dry, and dusty driveway, and drops me off. She's gone again before the billowing clouds of dust that trail behind her catch up.

I let myself in through the back door of the farmhouse, move to the dining room table, and sit down without saying a word. Guy, Derris, Jon, and Eva are about half finished with their evening meal.

"Come on, Robin, what's left of the green beans are still good," Aunt Eva encourages me. "I picked them just before dinner. There's a little bit of mashed potatoes and a couple of chicken wings and a thigh left. You can make a meal out of that. I was just about to serve peach cobbler for dessert. Surely you'll want some of that."

"How come you're late?" Derris asks. "Wasn't the usual sermon long enough to save everyone?"

I'm oblivious, staring into space, struggling with my

demons and with voices from both my past and present. I desperately need solitude.

"Religious claptrap destroys a lot of people," Guy says to Derris. "I didn't believe it at first, but with the psychiatrist and all, I suspect this is different. Derris, you're going to have to do Robin's chores again this evening."

"Take me to church," Derris says. "I'd like to get out of doing chores, even for a day."

I would gladly trade places with him if my mission were not a direct and sacred assignment from God.

"Don't complain. Robin needs our help. Jon will work with you."

The remainder of the conversation over dessert is like white noise. I sit at the table for the balance of the meal—eating, but not tasting; hearing the table talk, but not understanding. I am caught up in the complaints of Satan's demons, and the barrage of comments from others. Their words become my own thoughts that bounce around uncontrollably within my outer mind.

Once they finish their peach cobbler, the men leave the table to do their chores.

Anxiety, like my demons, is now a constant companion. I move from chair to chair, trying to escape. I begin to bang my head on the dinner table in an effort to distract myself from unrelenting voices and the burning of my anxiety.

"Robin!" Eva cries. "What are you doing? You'll hurt yourself."

Eva tries to put her arm around me. I pull away.

Running into the parlor, I sit curled up into a tight ball at one end of the couch, frequently pounding the cushions with my fists.

The men return after completing their chores. They can see me curled up on the couch like a porcupine under attack, but clearly don't understand my behavior.

"Music soothes the savage beast," Guy says. "Derris, get your saxophone."

Eva plays the upright piano, while Derris follows along on his horn and Guy plays the old mandolin his father left him. They play country western and hillbilly songs, singing along enthusiastically. Although I know they don't understand what's happening to me, I realize they are doing this for me because they care about me despite my bizarre behavior. They're trying to help me in any way they can. No questions asked; no strings attached. This selfless act, more than anything else, is genuinely soothing.

Soon it is bedtime, but I sleep little that night and for the balance of the week. I take to roaming the fields in the dead of night, searching for understanding.

19

The primary focus of my nightly wanderings is to determine Hugh's true identity. Is he one of Satan's demons or a gift from God? It's essential that I get the full measure of him, and to figure out as nearly as possible what role, if any, he might play in the completion of my mission. I also hope that learning this, I can discover more of what my mission is all about.

Even after three days on the farm, the voices of individuals I'd heard on the streets of Spokane continue to echo within my mind, along with a multitude of comments from others, both past and present.

When I close my eyes, I can still see the faces of many of the innocent "owners" of these voices. The voices echo within my outer mind and rightly or wrongly become part of my thinking. I wonder if Satan is in control of them all, at least in terms of letting them enter my mind unobstructed. It also occurs to me that some of these voices might contain hidden clues or gifts that God has somehow induced Satan to deliver to me unwittingly. In particular, the parishioners' voices continue their demands.

Aunt Eva's voice, along with the voices of Guy, Derris and Jon, have all joined in the chorus. The presence of their voices is comforting, however, even though they are fighting for a foothold in my outer mind just like all the others. What separates their voices, what makes them distinctive, is that their owners, along with Dr. Levy, accept me as I am without prejudice and without placing demands on me. The continuing and constant clamor of all the voices careening around inside my outer mind is wearing me down, sapping my strength.

"Hugh, the constant chatter is becoming too much for me again. Why haven't you invited me back into the safety of our inner mind?"

"You're no longer in imminent danger," Hugh replies. "To complete your mission you must do so in the outside world despite the pressures and chaos you're experiencing."

"It is unconscionable that God allows all this abuse to rain down upon you in the name of your 'sacred mission,'" Two interjects. "The peace and other blessings offered by our Master are immediately available. You're a fool to resist Him for the sake of a God that mistreats you."

"But it is Satan, your Master, who has destroyed the shell that protects my outer mind from these destructive intrusions. This is his fault."

"It's a matter of chastisement," One replies. "By refusing the destiny he's offered, you have forced him to use more extreme measures to get your attention."

The only saving grace in all this is that while I'm on the farm, the thoughts of Guy, Eva, Derris, and Jon are the only ones that have been added to my burden. Still, all the ones that came before them remain and continue to disrupt my life immeasurably. I'm coming to realize that I might be better off if I were never to leave the farm. But what would this mean for the church and my relationships with God and my family? This is deeply disturbing.

"Hugh, I don't think I can handle this much longer."

"You must!" Hugh says.

"How long will it be before I discover the proof that you're part of me and not one of Satan's demons?"

"You'll find the truth within us, within our heart, mind, and soul. When you gain this insight, the nature of our mission will begin to emerge and you'll discover we are one and the same person."

As on previous nights, after everyone has gone to bed, regardless of how quiet I am, the light in the kitchen goes on shortly after I leave the farmhouse. Experience teaches me that once I start back, sometimes many hours later, the light will go out. Obviously, someone is standing watch.

It's now Thursday night. I'm to see Dr. Levy in the morning. I walk along the eastern field at the edge of the forest. The moon reflects enough light to prevent me from stumbling over gopher mounds or falling into the old well that is somewhere along the way. Thousands of stars twinkle in the black sky above and there's a light breeze.

"You know it's a pain in the ass following you around all night," Three complains.

"I'm glad you're having fun. You're always bragging about being available twenty-four hours a day, seven days a week. It's only been three days and you're ready to bail out. It's ironic that your beloved Master is the one who is causing your discomfort. How does it feel to be the victim of his wrath?"

"The real question," Two observes philosophically, *"is why must we suffer when our Leader is punishing you?"*

I step on a branch that is much like a crack. I stamp my right foot three times and tap my right toe behind me.

As I have each night before, I start my deliberations by trying to summarize what I've figured out about Hugh.

My intuition tells me that Hugh is a special part of me and not a separate person, and that special part of me has found refuge in the newly formed inner portion of our mind where he's safe. I know I won't be able to figure out what part of me Hugh has taken with him into my inner mind and how much of the original me remains with Robin. Although I have strong feelings about this, I'm not sure I can rely on them. It might just be wishful thinking.

Also, Hugh says that he's been assigned to preserve us, but not necessarily protect Robin. What does this mean and why has God chosen to help me in this way?

"I think you've arrived at a point in your deliberations where I might be able to answer at least some of your questions," Hugh says.

"Then I'd like to ask."

"So ask away."

"You've said that we are one and the same person and that we share precisely the same experience and information. How is it then that you can answer questions that I can't answer for myself?"

"It's simply a matter of the different functions for which we are responsible," Hugh says.

"Must you always speak in riddles?"

"For starters, Robin, your job is to deal with the outside world with all its complications. You must remain focused on the here and now. You make decisions and take immediate action. You can only keep a tiny portion of our experience and knowledge within your consciousness at any given time."

"My primary function," Hugh continues, "is to seek out and preserve the truth. Because I don't have to deal with the everyday

250

world as you do, I can spend much more time contemplating the truth. I can focus on this for extended periods without interruption."

"That's pretty abstract. Do you actually do anything?"

"I do a great deal," Hugh replies. "One of my functions is an analytical one. I analyze the information that comes from your encounters in the everyday world. I've ongoing access to all this information in the form of memories, most of which are stored in our inner mind. Once you commit your experiences to memory within our inner mind, you move on to other things related to our survival in the real world and this information passes out of your consciousness and thinking. In fact, your intuitions and insights often originate with me."

"But I have access to my memories."

"That's true," Hugh replies. "But you can only keep a small portion of these memories in your consciousness at any given time. I have access to all of it at once. That's why it appears I can answer questions that you can't."

"Hugh, I have a couple of additional questions. Why have you chosen to announce your presence, even your existence, to me now?"

"I've done this because you've been taught inconsistent 'truths' all your life. This has resulted in serious conflicts in your beliefs, even your entire belief system. But you have refused to acknowledge these conflicts. As a consequence, your belief system, which is affecting your behavior, is in shambles. This is what has brought about the vicious assaults by Satan and his minions and placed you in great danger. All this must be sorted out if you're to complete your mission. The first part of your mission is to find the truth and my function is to make sure that you do."

"I'll have to think about all this. But let me ask another question. What do you mean when you say you're here to preserve us and not necessarily to protect me?"

"You need to figure this out for yourself," Hugh says. "But I have a hint I can give you. Remember that my primary function is to discover and preserve the truth."

I continue my journey along the edge of the fields trying to figure out the meaning of Hugh's clue. Over the next two hours, I completely circle the farmhouse. By this time, I'm exhausted and about ready to give up. But when I arrive back at my starting point, it comes to me. It's an insight that seems to flash within my mind like the burst of a strobe light, a revelation from God. My mind soars and my body seems to float on air. To make sure my insight makes sense, that this isn't one of Satan's tricks, I need to talk with someone who understands the importance of it, someone who knows about my mission.

I get back to the farmhouse shortly before 3 a.m., just as the light in the kitchen goes out. I sleep soundly for the first night in weeks. At last I'm beginning to figure out the nature of my mission. Eva lets me sleep in until just before Mother arrives to take me to my Friday morning appointment with Dr. Levy.

I try to explain to Dr. Levy everything that happened with Hugh the night before. He listens intently, asks several questions, and makes notes in my file.

"It seems to me that your conversation with Hugh raises more questions than it answers," Dr. Levy observes.

"You're right. After I talked with Hugh, I realized I had several questions I think are important. When my walk ended, I had a sudden insight that answered a lot of them."

"What are the questions?"

"The first one is why does Hugh think it's essential to distance himself so completely from any direct involvement in Robin's ongoing struggle with Satan and his demons? Why can't Hugh leave our inner mind to protect Robin? After all, he's made a point of the fact that Robin must remain in our outer mind where he is dangerously exposed. It occurred to me that there's something Hugh isn't telling me. Also, why does Hugh insist he's primarily 'concerned with preserving us,' whatever that means?"

"Hugh is bogus," Two says. "He's a product of your imagination. Questions you may have concerning what this imaginary character may say or do are a complete waste of your time and ours."

"It seems to me," Dr. Levy begins, "that the answers to the questions you just raised are all clustered around the fact that Hugh isn't willing to risk himself to protect Robin."

"Remember," I say, "Robin's function is to deal with the real world and Hugh's function is to seek out the truth, which must also involve managing our relationship with God."

"And you have always maintained your relationship with God is of paramount importance to you," Dr. Levy adds.

"Bingo! That's the answer, at least in part!"

"What's the answer?" Dr. Levy asks, looking both surprised and puzzled.

"Robin is expendable, and Hugh is not."

"What?"

"What will happen if Robin is lost in battle?"

"What do you mean?" Dr. Levy asks. His curiosity is obvious.

"What if Robin becomes dysfunctional? What if he loses his identity?"

"I'm not certain," Dr. Levy responds. "But you have

consistently maintained that the continued existence of the universe is dependent on the completion of your mission, on you defeating Satan."

"Don't you see it? Even if Robin loses his battle with Satan, his essence, his beliefs, will remain intact in the person of Hugh. Robin is expendable, but Hugh isn't. In other words, if Hugh is preserved, Robin can't be destroyed because his beliefs will remain intact. Hugh must not be exposed to Satan. It's why he must stay in our inner mind where he's fully protected. Hugh represents my beliefs and the truth as I see it. He must not be destroyed."

"That puts Robin in a lousy position," Dr. Levy observes.

"Does it? Knowing this, Robin can put everything he's got into his battle with Satan. He can take significant risks. In doing so, he'll have the assurance that the truth for which he is fighting will live on in Hugh even if Robin himself becomes lost, either temporarily or permanently. And, because Hugh is, in essence, my beliefs, Hugh can choose to recreate the essence of Robin at any time or let him lie inactive even for a lifetime. This renders 'Robin' indestructible as well."

"This would seem to make some sense," Dr. Levy says, "but isn't it a circular argument?"

"Do you mean like the circle of life?"

"Hugh lives in your inner mind and that mind resides within your brain. What happens when you die or if your brain is destroyed?"

"All of our bodies eventually die, but the truth lives on. The duration of Robin's mission may be limited to Robin's lifetime, but as long as Hugh survives until Robin's death whatever Robin's condition may be, even if Robin has been inactive for an extended period, the truth remains. Upon my death, God must invest that truth in another person if the truth that Hugh holds is to become part of my legacy. In other words, Robin may pass away, but the truths he has found and invested in Hugh will endure and be invested in others if they learn these truths from him."

"But why then is your mission and you—the current Robin—essential to the survival of the universe?" Dr. Levy asks. "It seems to me that God has stacked the deck, and God will always prevail. It seems that you can't fail. The truth will never be lost."

"Oh, but I can fail. If I give in to Satan, if I agree to become one of his minions, I will be denying Hugh and the truths he holds; then Satan has won and the universe will end."

"There's still something you're not telling me."

Dr. Levy's challenge catches me off guard. Suddenly vulnerable, I hug my chest and lean forward to protect myself from what I think might be coming.

How does he always know?

"Has the congregation assaulted you again?"

Dr. Levy's voice is now gentle, reassuring.

This is going to be hard, but I need to talk to someone, and Dr. Levy is the only one who will understand.

I force myself to sit upright and face the doctor.

"I know these assaults are traumatic," Dr. Levy says, "but if you know the truth, you'll be fine."

"Hugh, do you promise to reveal the truth to me?"

"You must take the first steps so you can be certain of the validity of anything I tell you," Hugh replies. "I can assist you once you've made some progress on your own."

"I'm no longer sure what is true and what is false. All my life I've never had any doubts, but now I'm so confused."

Unwittingly or not, Dr. Levy has just touched on the crux of the problem on which I'm now focused. My face flushes red. Coldness rises from deep within me. I begin to sweat.

"For as long as I can remember, I've been taught that salvation is a gift from God, that there is nothing we can do to save ourselves. But I've also been taught that I must believe in God to be saved. Which is it? Is there nothing I can do to be saved, or must I believe to be saved?"

Sitting up straight again, I make no further attempt to hide my tears.

"Telling Dr. Levy about this is dangerous," Two warns.

I watch Dr. Levy closely, but can't read his reaction. I continue anyway.

"I'm beginning to wonder if I even control my own mind."

"Is he finally beginning to accept the truth?" Three asks. His voice is hopeful.

Dr. Levy's eyes reveal his surprise. This is very unusual.

"What makes you say that?"

"I can't control my own thoughts."

"I don't understand. It seems to me you've been quite successful in fighting off Satan and his demons, and the members of the church as well. I think your efforts demonstrate that you have a great deal of self-control."

"But is the fact that all this has occurred in the first place my fault? Am I somehow deficient, somehow unworthy?"

"What?" Dr. Levy asks, looking puzzled.

"Do you really think I've been successful?"

"I think so."

"You'd be lost without our assistance," Two remarks.

"Your assistance is a trap. You're constantly trying to mislead me."

"Well, I don't. Satan, when he's here, and my demons and whomever they bring into my mind, like the members of the church, all control my thoughts."

Dr. Levy seems unperturbed.

"Do they control your thoughts? Or do they just confuse you?"

He's not passing judgment. I think I can safely discuss this with him.

"Both."

"But surely you decide what you think," Dr. Levy says.

"No, I don't. Others are now involved—Satan, his demons, and everyone they bring in with them."

"Now wait just a minute," Two says. "We reason with you, providing advice. That's not 'controlling.'"

"What do you mean?" Dr. Levy asks.

"Well, pretend you are One. You and I are sitting here talking, right? It's just like my conversations with One that take place all the time in my mind. You say something like, 'My cat is black.' I hear that and it becomes a thought of mine."

"Are you saying everything One says becomes one of your own thoughts?"

"Yes, I do think it, don't I? When someone says, 'My cat is black,' I hear it, and precisely because I hear it, I'm also thinking 'My cat is black.' To hear it is to think it."

"The congregation may have succeeded in driving you mad," Three jeers.

"But that doesn't mean you believe it," Dr. Levy says.

"It doesn't matter whether I believe it or not. I'm still thinking the thought."

"I think our young protagonist is having a mental meltdown," Three remarks.

"I'm not having a mental meltdown!"

"What? Dr. Levy asks.

"You're so confused, you don't know who you're talking to," Three jeers.

"Shut up. I'm trying to talk to Dr. Levy."

"Well, excuse me," Three snaps.

"What if my cat is white?" Dr. Levy asks.

"How would I know? I've never seen your cat."

Dr. Levy looks puzzled, so I continue.

"Don't you see? What you said about your cat being black becomes one of my thoughts even if it's not true, and regardless of whether or not I believe it. That's the crux of the problem. I'm thinking things that aren't true and may not even realize they're false."

"But as you just said, the thoughts aren't true."

"Exactly! So how can I believe anything I think? The ideas of my demons and their stooges, true or false, become part of my thinking."

Dr. Levy swivels in his chair and looks out the window as he often does when struggling with one of my comments.

What if Dr. Levy can't help me? What if there is no medication that will help me?

I feel myself sinking as if in quicksand, the weight of my fears pulling me down.

"We have reasoned with you," One said. "We don't need to coerce you because we know you'll eventually see the truth."

"But Satan puts thoughts directly into my mind. He uses my own voice."

"He's only trying to bring you to your senses, to demonstrate his powers."

Sweat trickles down the back of my neck.

Dr. Levy swivels back around to face me.

"But you have your own thoughts," he continues, "certainly your own beliefs."

"I get so confused. The ideas of these others are in my mind just like my own thoughts, my own beliefs. They get jumbled together. Sometimes I can't tell them apart. The thoughts I do originate get mixed in with everyone else's thoughts. I don't know what's true and what's not. I just don't know what to believe."

"You have your precious God to thank for that," Three says.

Dr. Levy makes a tent with his fingers and looks at me over the top, his brow furrowed.

"The truth is I don't know who I am. If my thoughts aren't my own, where do I begin and end? Where's the dividing line between me and other people?"

"See, God is trying to drive you insane!" Two declares.

"Do you mean that sometimes you don't know who you are, or that the boundaries between you and others are becoming a blur?"

"Both. But even more important, I'm not sure who I'm becoming."

"What do you mean by who you are becoming?"

"I know I'm changing."

"This ought to be good." Three interjects.

Dr. Levy leans forward and puts his elbows on his desk.

"Satan and my demons claim I'm becoming one of them. If I become one of them, I'll most certainly have given in to Satan and the universe will end. They know I won't do it willingly, but what happens if I don't know who I am? If I don't know who I am and therefore what I believe, I might give in to Satan and not even realize it."

"And you're sure Satan is doing this?"

"Yes, I'm becoming everyone, at least all those who gain access to my mind, and it could lead me to fail at my mission."

Dr. Levy gets up and turns to look out the window, his hands behind his back.

I wait.

After a few minutes, Dr. Levy turns back around and looks into my eyes.

"The medication you are taking has helped, hasn't it?" Dr. Levy asks.

"Yes."

"I'd like to increase the dosage if you're up to it."

"Do you think that will help?"

"I don't know," Dr. Levy replies, "but I think it's worth trying."

"Beware!" Two cautions. "The good doctor is experimenting! We've warned you about this."

"Will it make me groggy?"

"It might, at least for a few days."

"Will it help me remember who I am, even though I'm changing?"

I think of George from the hospital and his fear of forgetting the names of his children.

"We are what we believe," Dr. Levy says. "And when our beliefs are changing, it's often confusing and sometimes a little disturbing."

"Will I forget what I believe?"

"If you forget what you believe, then it is no longer a part of you," Dr. Levy replies.

"This is scary, but I'll try it as long as Hugh remains safe within my inner mind."

20

"Well, what do you think you'll be doing this week?" Mother asks as we race along the country road that would eventually return me to Guy and Eva's.

"Just chores," I reply.

I'm beginning to feel a little better since my conversation with Dr. Levy that morning. I'm hopeful that the increase in my medication will help.

Mother looks at me as if she expects more of a response.

"We'll probably be working in the woods again," I say. "When we've finished gathering timbers for the new corral, we'll start cutting cordwood for the winter."

"What else?" Mother asks.

"Guy lets us ride our horses at dusk every day. It's a lot of fun."

"And how's the horse?"

Mother never refers to Shady by name, or even gender. Shady will always be just the "horse." Mother has never fully resigned herself to my spending the weekends on the farm. Still, she has stopped arguing about it. She's even willing to drive me back and forth for my meetings with Dr. Levy, but it's clear she hasn't given up on getting me involved again with the church. She leaves me with the impression she's trying to come up with a more convincing reason why I should attend services or other church activities.

"Shady is just fine. I'm going to practice roping again this week. But it's discouraging. Shady gets frustrated with me. I can't even lasso a fence post, let alone a calf on the loose. She just stops and stamps her hooves when I miss."

"You'll get the hang of it. Just think positively."

My mission is a figment of my imagination.

Where did that come from?

The idea that God would give me a mission is preposterous.

What am I thinking?

Just as everyone claims, I am insane.

My whole body stiffens.

"No, absolutely not!"

God help me! Satan is putting thoughts into my mind again.

"Go away."

"Whatever gave you the idea you can control your own thoughts, that you own your mind? Your quack doctor is

ignorant. You're at my mercy. You always have been. Get used to it."

It feels like my legs are going to cramp. I try to extend them, but the dashboard is in the way.

"I will not accept your claims."

"I can tell you what to think at any time. One of the things they taught you in that horrid parochial school was correct. 'We are what we think.'"

"We may be what we think, but I'll not accept the thoughts you put into my mind!"

"No? How naïve you are. Why do I waste my time with you? You will soon discover I can control all your thoughts and you'll be whatever I decide to make of you."

"That's simply not true."

My mind is now focused like a spotlight. It isn't pain but fear that channels my thoughts.

"Just ignore him," Hugh says. "He's bluffing."

"We'll talk about this again in the future, when you've come to recognize the truth," Satan says. **"Why do you make it so hard for yourself?"**

"I won't give in to you."

"My mission is a figment of my imagination."

No!

I will ignore the thoughts Satan puts into my mind.

"You'll never control me," I shout, but Satan is already gone.

Mother jerks at the steering wheel as she swings her head around to look at me. She swerves across the center line toward an oncoming car.

"Mom, look out!"

The horn of the approaching car blares.

Mother overcompensates and swerves onto the right shoulder of the road. Plowing through the gravel with the brakes on all four wheels locked, the car finally comes skidding to a halt.

"Don't ever do that again," Mother exclaims. "You could have gotten us killed."

"I'm sorry, Mom."

"Why did you shout at me?" Mother demands.

"I wasn't thinking."

"No, you most certainly were not!"

Mother checks for traffic and pulls back onto the road.

Several minutes pass before she speaks again.

"You know you're missing a lot by spending weekends on the farm."

I've known this would come sooner or later. But there's no way I'm going to our new church. Dr. Levy's right. I'm better off on the farm.

"The youth group is quite active on the weekends and the kids are so nice," Mother says. "Did you know they all went water-skiing last Sunday?"

It's clear to me now that most of the adults in the church

are possessed by Satan's demons. Chances are good that their kids are possessed by demons as well. The universe is at stake with my mission and Satan will go to any extreme.

"I'm not interested in the youth group."

"Are you sure? I've told them all about you. They're looking forward to meeting you."

They're possessed by Satan's demons. Of course, they're anxious to meet me. I wonder if Satan is offering a reward to the demon that destroys my mission.

"Why don't you stay home next weekend and just meet them?" Mother pleads.

"My mission is sacred, Mother. Why would I want to jeopardize it and the entire universe by exposing myself to a whole host of Satan's demons? They are extremely dangerous."

Mother turns and stares. Out of the corner of my eye, I can see her expression turn from shock to confusion to fear.

"What in the world are you talking about, Robin? These are high school children."

"Nothing's what it seems, Mother."

We've taken baths, waxed our crew cuts, and cleaned our fingernails. Guy insists we all use his aftershave. With our boots shined, clean jeans, and fancy country shirts freshly washed and pressed by Eva, we are all gussied up for the 4H Thursday night dance.

I had begged Guy to let me stay on the farm. I didn't tell him I'm afraid of accumulating more unwanted voices. I even offer to do some additional chores while the rest of them are away.

He says that I've been working hard and, like the rest of them, I deserve a "night on the town." He insists that I go.

Guy parks the car in a vacant spot in the field behind the 4H Club dance hall. We walk around the side of the building toward the entrance in front, taking care not to muddy our boots. We can hear the ending strains of "My Old Kentucky Home."

I've never been to a dance before. Will I have to dance? I don't know how. A sense of foreboding makes me uncomfortable. The closer we get to the front door, the worse it becomes.

We pass by a group of young men leaning against their pickups with bottles of beer in their hands and cigarettes hanging from their mouths. Their conversations stop as we walk past.

Guy holds the door open as first Eva, then Derris, Jon, and I enter the dance hall. The band has apparently just finished its first set. The band members are climbing down from the platform and heading for the bar.

"What do you think, Mark?"

"She's a good-looking heifer. I'd put my brand on her any day of the week."

I look around to see who is speaking, but none of the young men milling about are close enough for me to hear any of them speak. Yet I am hearing their thoughts.

Like the voices of the Holy Cross members, Satan has let these into my outer mind without introduction. I'm not able to match these voices with their owners, yet their every word tortures me. Satan has obviously decided to increase the pressure on me. My sense of foreboding is rapidly increasing, threatening to generate an attack of anxiety.

"What do you guys want?" Guy asks.

"I want to go home."

Guy ignores my comment.

"You guys wait here," Guy says. "Come on, Eva. Let's get us a stiff drink and some coke for the boys."

"He's the oldest. He'll get the farm."

All the girls are standing along the far wall, but somehow I can hear them talking from across the room.

"It's the biggest dairy farm in the county, you know. Any girl that finally hog-ties Frank will be sitting pretty."

The conversations throughout the entire dance hall now ring in my ears.

"I don't want your mother moving in, Louise. Do you want to spend all your time taking care of her? What about the kids?"

"George, I've said this before and I'll say it again…"

"I don't want your mother moving in, Louise. Do you…"

God help me! I'm acquiring new voices yet again.

"But can any girl keep him corralled for long?"

And now I'm picking up yet another voice. This evening is going to be a disaster.

"Ellen doesn't seem to be concerned about keeping her hold on him."

I'm trapped. I'm now thinking what everyone is saying. Everyone else's thoughts are becoming my own.

"It's not too late," One says. "Accept out Master."

"Never!"

"Look at all the young ladies," Guy says. "Derris, get over there and ask one of them to dance."

Derris looks like a deer in headlights.

"Look who just came in."

"Ask one of the girls to dance," Guy repeats. He gives Derris a shove.

"Isn't that Guy's boy? He's just a baby. What's he doing here? What's his name?"

"We tried to warn you about talking to your shrink," Three shrieks. *"Now we'll all have to pay."*

"Ellen, I think his name is Derris. Or something that sounds like Derris."

I begin to panic.

"Remember, I'm here to preserve us," Hugh says.

"Hugh, I don't mean to sound ungrateful, but right now I need protection."

"You must learn how to deal with Satan's treachery no matter what form it takes."

"Well, Derris looks like he's in shock. It's about time he learns to dance. I'm going to give him one of my special dances, like the ones I save for Frank. We'll see how fast he grows up."

The young women around Ellen burst into laughter.

270

"I'd be careful, Ellen. Frank's going to get all pissed off if he sees you teasing the kid."

Ellen works her way across the room, dodging dancers, both young and old, who are gliding and swirling in a fog of cigarette smoke. She heads straight for Derris.

"Are you Derris?" Ellen asks sweetly. "I've heard a lot about you."

Derris' mouth drops open.

"Come on, Derris, let's dance."

Ellen takes Derris' hand and leads him onto the dance floor.

Guy and Eva return with drinks.

"Well, take a look at that," Guy says. "Derris is dancing."

"See, Robin! It isn't so hard," Guy says. "You're next."

"There's going be trouble if Frank sees this," one of the girls observes. "Let Ellen get started with the kid and then we'll go get Frank."

I don't want to hear this. Why is this happening?

"Haven't you figured it out by now?" Two asks.

I concentrate, trying to block out the thoughts of all the others.

Why is my hearing suddenly so good?

"Are you having trouble with your hearing?" Satan hisses. "Perhaps it's become too good?"

"I tried to warn you," One says.

"I decided if you won't listen to me," Satan says, "you might enjoy listening to everyone else. I've made it easier for you."

"What have you done to me?"

"Remember, we are what we think. Even your wretched parochial school taught you that. Or perhaps it's 'who' we think."

Satan's laugh is more like a growl.

"You'll figure it out in time," Satan says. "I'm sorry, but I must run. Enjoy yourself, whoever you are."

Satan has just departed when I hear a commotion on the dance floor. Frank pushes Derris aside and grabs Ellen by the arm. The band stops playing in the middle of "Setting the Woods on Fire," a song by Hank Williams, one that Aunt Eva often plays.

"Just who do you think you're messing with, Ellen?" Frank shouts. "I can't believe this. He's just a kid."

An uneasy hush falls over the room.

"I didn't do anything," Ellen says, mocking Frank.

"She asked me to dance," Derris pleads. "Honest."

Guy is pushing his way through the crowd, trying to get to Derris, who's still standing in the middle of the dance floor.

The crowd parts in front of them as Frank drags Ellen off the dance floor and toward the exit. Suddenly, everyone is talking at once.

Standing at the edge of the dance floor, I'm in the middle of all the commotion. The voices of everyone in the dance hall rain down on me. The chaos washes over me like a tidal wave. I'm feeling nauseated.

"Hugh, please help me."

Hugh doesn't respond.

I'm left with no choice. As I force my outer mind to close, to shut down completely, everything around me fades to black. I feel my body collapse. In what seems like slow motion, I drop to the floor.

"Good morning, Robin," Dr. Levy says. "I understand Guy and Eva took you to a 4H dance last night. Did you enjoy it?"

It's not a good morning. Everything is so confusing.

"Robin?"

"Robin's not here."

"Robin's not here?"

"No."

"Who's talking with me then?"

"I am everyone."

"I'm hoping to talk to Robin about what happened last night at the dance."

"But I'm everyone."

"Why am I talking to everyone? Has Robin taken refuge somewhere?"

"He's not hiding in his inner mind, if that's what you mean! Hugh won't let him."

Realizing that I had again been caught off guard by Dr.

Levy's grasp of my situation, I try to organize my thoughts.

"Until Robin can control his own thoughts, until Robin can decide what he himself believes," I say, "I'm everyone I encounter, everyone I hear, because everyone's thoughts become my own."

"How can I talk to everyone?" Dr. Levy asks.

"Would you like me to be someone in particular? I can be whomever you want me to be."

"Why would I want you to be anyone other than Robin?"

"Robin is lost. Like I said, I can't be Robin any more until I know which thoughts are Robin's and which are the thoughts of others. Until then, I'm everyone."

"I don't want to talk to everyone."

"I know. I'll be Vice President Richard Nixon. I saw myself on TV last week. I warned everyone about the communist menace. Did you know that the communists are…?"

"But I want to talk to Robin," Dr. Levy interrupts.

"We won't hear from Robin until he knows what he believes."

"How do we determine what Robin believes?"

"We'll have to talk to him about that."

"How can we get to Robin?"

"We must find something Robin believes in and work from that to find the rest of him."

"Well, Robin believes in softball. Can Robin and I talk

about softball?"

"You can talk to all of me who believe in softball. There are many of us."

"I find this very confusing," Dr. Levy says.

"I know. I'll be Coach. We can talk about last week's game. Holy Cross lost to Xavier by 4 to 2. We're 2 and 3 on the season."

"No, I want to talk to Robin about softball."

"Robin's not sure he believes in softball anymore because not everyone he hears believes in softball. He's so confused."

"Then I'd like to talk to Robin about horses."

"Many of us believe in horses, but then, many of us do not."

"Robin believes in horses. Can I talk to Robin about horses?"

"He's not sure he believes in horses anymore, so he can't talk to you about horses. Besides, others believe in horses. You'll have to talk to all of me who do."

Dr. Levy, clearly baffled and frustrated, gets out of his chair and turns to look out the window.

Minutes pass.

I wait.

Abruptly, Dr. Levy turns around.

"I want to talk to Robin about his mission."

"Good morning, Dr. Levy," Robin says.

"Robin, do you know where you are?

"Yes."

"Can we talk about the 4H dance you went to last night?"

"It was terrifying."

I get up and pace back and forth twice, then sit down. Getting up again, I immediately sit down. I just can't sit still.

"I think your experience has left you anxious."

"It's like hot lava under my skin trying to force its way to the surface."

"Do you feel like you want to 'jump out of your skin'?" Dr. Levy asks.

"Yes. If only I could."

"Robin, it sounds like you're suffering from a bout of clinical anxiety."

"What's that?"

"It's different from just being uneasy, or worried, or 'antsy' about something. Most people experience a touch of that every day over one thing or another. Clinical anxiety is more severe. It's much more uncomfortable, constant and lasts longer, sometimes for days or even weeks. A lot of things can trigger a bout of clinical anxiety, like the 4H dance last night, but it's a physiological problem. It has to do with brain chemistry."

"Is there some kind of medication I should be taking?"

"Hiding behind your medication isn't going to work any longer," One says. "Our Benefactor is losing his patience. It's time you joined us in our allegiance to Him."

"We have two choices. One is to give you a sedative for a few days. The other is to increase the dosage of your present medication."

"I don't want a sedative. It turns me into a vegetable. I sleep all the time."

I can't afford to lose any more time or memories. It would only leave me more confused.

"Then we should consider increasing the dosage of your medication again," Dr. Levy says.

"But whenever we increase the dose, it makes me groggy."

"But the grogginess usually disappears within a week or so, doesn't it?"

"Yes."

"Which would you prefer?"

"If you think we need to do something, then increasing my medication would be better."

"Tell me," Dr. Levy continues, "what would happen if your anxiety broke through to the surface of your skin?"

"It could kill me. Or even worse, I might become one of them."

"On the contrary, you would begin to realize your destiny," Two says.

"Have you been trying to trigger clinical anxiety in me?"

"Of course not," One protests. "We've been trying to work with you to help you fully appreciate what our Master has in store for you."

"The destiny your demons have in store for us is far worse than any bout of clinical anxiety," Hugh says. "They've been trying to convince you that God has abandoned you. They're not to be trusted."

"I already know that."

"We haven't denied that some aspects of your preparation may be uncomfortable," Two says.

"What do you mean when you say, 'you might become one of them'?" Dr. Levy asks. "Are you talking about becoming one of Satan's followers?"

"I might become a demon."

Just imagine the powers and privileges our Leader would bestow upon you," One says. "You'd have no equal."

"They'll do or promise anything to ensnare us," Hugh warns.

"Tell me something I don't already know."

"You know that I only know what you know," Hugh replies. "It's entirely a matter of focusing on the right things."

"Then lead me to something I already know, but haven't focused on before."

"You know you must find what to focus on by yourself. I can't help you."

"No wonder you're anxious," Dr. Levy says. "Is there anything more?"

I squirm in my chair. My skin is burning as if I were badly sunburned. I wonder if Hugh can feel this.

I feel the hot, foul breath of my three demons on the back of my neck.

This has never happened before! They've never appeared to have a physical presence. They must be terrified. It's clearly dangerous to talk about this. But is it dangerous for me or for them?

My face in my hands, I sob quietly. I feel as if I've been physically battered. Pains shoot up and down my back. My ribs hurt whenever I move. My arms hurt when I touch them as if they are bruised.

"Take your time, Robin."

"Haven't my assistants warned you?" Satan growls. *"This subject is not to be discussed with your precious shrink."*

Satan is back. I've been afraid that he would return.

"I'm running out of patience with you. You are becoming too costly in time and attention. If you don't comply with my wishes, I'll take you straight to hell here and now."

I stand up to run, but there's no place to go. I sit back down.

"Don't listen to Satan," Hugh says. "He has no real power over us."

Something hits me hard in the stomach. I double over in pain, slide out of my chair, and sink to my knees.

Dr. Levy leaps out of his chair and comes around to my side of his desk, kneeling next to me.

"Breathe deeply," he commands. "Take slow, even breaths."

"You've always been mine and always will be mine," Satan says. *"It's your destiny to serve me."*

"No!" I gasp in firm denial.

"Satan is back, isn't he?" Dr. Levy asks.

"Yes."

"Can you tell me what's happening to you?" Dr. Levy says, his voice full of concern.

"You'll regret this for all eternity," Satan hisses in frustration. His voice is clear, but only a whisper.

"I'm okay, Dr. Levy."

"Are you sure that you're all right?" Dr. Levy presses.

Before I leave Dr. Levy's office, he writes a script for a higher dosage of my medication.

21

"Robin, I know everything's been better on the farm and that it's only been a couple of weeks since the 4H dance, but do you think you can handle the 4ᵗʰ of July at home?" Dr. Levy asks. "Or would you feel more comfortable staying on the farm?"

"Remember, there are now many of us. I am everyone. Should I take a vote? You know the majority rules and all that. But then again, I'm not sure how many of me there are, so I don't know how many of me would make up a majority."

"Think about it for a minute," Dr. Levy says.

"I'm not sure what to do," I stammer.

"What do you think, Hugh?"

"I think it'll be all right as long as it's just our parents and Carl," Hugh says. "We don't want to add any new voices, good or bad, because that'll further complicate our mission."

"It's an important decision," Dr. Levy continues, "but since we recently increased the dose of your medication, that may help."

"Who'll be there?"

"Just your brother and parents," Dr. Levy replies. "Your mother agreed that no one else will be invited or allowed to visit, so you don't need to worry about accumulating new voices."

"Can I go back to the farm if things get out of hand?"

"I think your mother will agree to that," Dr. Levy offers.

Mom, Dad and Carl pick me up at the farm about 9 a.m. The drive back to Spokane takes about forty-five minutes.

"Where are we going?" I ask with alarm. "We just passed our house."

"We're going where we always go on the 4th of July," Mother replies.

"Where do you mean?" I ask with suspicion. My muscles tense.

"Pay attention," Mother commands. "We're going to Marvin and Bea's."

Marvin, my mother's older brother, married Mildred, my father's younger sister. This meant that all the Schroeder kids, Carol, Ray and Larry, and the Cunningham kids, my older brother Carl and I, were double cousins. When Mildred got sick, Marvin, on the advice of Mildred's psychiatrist, divorced her.

Several years later, Marvin married Bea Eicherman, who had a son of her own by her previous husband. Her son's name was Gary Eicherman. But Bea also brought to the marriage two other children who were the children of her previous husband. These were Linda and Lynn Eicherman. All in all, Marvin and Bea raised six children.

Marvin and my mother were close, sharing many values they were taught by their parents.

"Mom, I can't go to Marvin and Bea's. You promised Dr. Levy."

"I promised Dr. Levy not to invite anyone to our house."

"Mom, you can't do this to me!"

"They're family. It won't hurt you to pay them a visit. You haven't seen your cousins in three months."

"This is not right!" Hugh exclaims. "We're not ready for this! You'll find yourself picking up even more voices."

I try to open the back door of the car to jump out, but it's locked.

Until called to the table for dinner, I hide in the basement of Marvin and Bea's house. I know if I don't show up for dinner, Mother will come looking and I'll find myself in trouble. When I enter the dining room, everyone is seated and waiting for me. Mother says nothing, but gives me a stern look. Uncle Marvin says a prayer of thanks and the meal gets underway.

"Wow! Did you see that last soup can take off when the 'Killer Blaster' I put under it blew?" my cousin Larry asks with enthusiasm. He stuffs a forkful of green beans in his mouth. "It went clear over the top of the maple tree!"

Suddenly, Larry's voice is in my outer mind, precisely reproduced in all its details of pitch and inflection.

"Larry, how many times do I have to tell you not to talk with your mouth full?" Aunt Bea admonishes.

Looking guilty, Larry stops chewing and sets his fork down.

Aunt Bea's voice has joined Larry's in my outer mind. I'm collecting new voices at an alarming rate.

"Hugh, this is exactly what we're supposed to avoid."

"Larry, you'd better start listening to what your mother says," Uncle Marvin scolds.

I put my hands over my ears. It doesn't help.

"Hugh, you've got to help. I can't afford to collect any more voices!"

Bang! Bang! Bang! Bang! Bang! I can still hear the firecrackers exploding over and over within my outer mind.

"Except in dire circumstances, I can't intervene," Hugh explains. "You must learn to deal with these voices on your own."

"Robin, please pass the potatoes," my cousin Ray says.

"But this is getting dangerous. What am I supposed to do?"

"I don't know any more than you do," Hugh replies.

"We warned you," One says. His voice was dripping with anger and fear. "You've opened the original Pandora's box. Our Benefactor's wrath…"

"It's not fair," Two complains. "After all we've done, all these voices now have free entry into Robin's outer mind. We no longer have control over them. They're interrupting us when we talk. This is making…"

"You have my sympathy."

"Your sympathy isn't going to help us," One cries. "We're

284

supposed to be your advisors. We need to be able to talk with you without interruption."

"Robin," Mother sighs. "Ray asked you to pass the mashed potatoes. Listen up."

"There's nothing I can do."

"But we're trying to help you. That should count…"

"It was your Master that destroyed the shell around my outer mind. He's the one who let all the voices in. He's the one who enhanced my sense of hearing, so don't try to blame me."

"Robin," Mother complains. "Pay attention."

"Well, I'm not one to complain," Hugh remarks. "The more time your demons spend dealing with their problems, the less time they have to harass us."

"We warned you not to tell your shrink about this imaginary person, this Hugh," Two reprimands. "None of this would have ever happened if you'd…"

"Robin!" Mother scolds. "Wake up and pass the potatoes to Ray or so help me I'll…"

"Now that it's happening to you, how do you like it?"

"One, Two and Three are obviously furious," Hugh says. "But they appear to be even more terrified."

"Hugh, this is making everything more difficult for me too. The fact that my misery has company doesn't seem to be helping."

"Lora," Marvin interjects, "I've told you that boy needs discipline. 'Spare the rod and spoil the child.' The problems you're having with Robin can be fixed with a hickory switch."

"Hugh, things are getting worse. The voices are accumulating. Even when they interrupt Satan's demons, they're crowding into my mind. They're piling one upon another, creating layer after layer, each voice demanding my undivided attention. And Satan's demons are getting desperate. Who knows what they might do?"

"I know," Hugh says.

"The voices never shut up. I'm getting confused. I can't hear myself think. Why aren't you affected by all the voices?"

"I hear them, but I'm in our inner mind and fully protected, so I can focus and think clearly even in those periods when you can't. When you're overwhelmed, you can rely on me to give you good advice. It's essential that you learn to depend on me."

"What can we do to make it easier for me?"

"You can take comfort in the fact that I'll carry on, that I'll preserve us. You must learn to trust me. Remember, we are one and the same. We have no conflicts of interest."

"Robin's off in never-never land," my cousin Carol observes. "He's getting weirder by the day."

"Carol," Bea scolds. "You need to be a little more understanding."

Marvin glares at Aunt Bea.

***"Your family will soon abandon you,"* One states matter-of-factly.*

"What did you say?"

***"Your family will soon abandon you,"* One repeats.*

"That's not true. My family will never do that!"

286

"And you once thought the church was your refuge," Three taunts. *"But now you know the parishioners would be happy if you never show your face in their church again. Your family will do no better by you than they have, no better than they did for Mildred."*

"Ever since the 4H Club dance, I've been hearing voices from across the room. All these voices continue to demand a private audience with me. If the only thing we can do is put up with this, Hugh, I don't think I'm going to last for very long."

"Calm down, kids," Marvin commands. "We're at the dinner table and you know the rules. 'Children are meant to be seen and not heard.'"

I remember Mildred's bitter complaint that Bea had stolen her children. This is not true, but with great sadness I can still feel Mildred's agony when she hugged me as if I were her own.

No matter the reason, Marvin has abandoned Mildred. Can this happen to me?

"You must take the initiative and break with them," Two insists, *"before they send you to Eastern State. You must get out of this mess on your own terms."*

"But, I'm not sick and you know it. Dr. Levy believes that I'll be all right."

"No one else believes in you," One declares.

"I do," Hugh says.

"Mom, Ray is taking seconds on the mashed potatoes and he's not leaving any for anyone else," Larry complains.

"Dr. Levy promised he'd never put me into Eastern State."

"And you believed him?" Two snickers. *"We've explained that he can change his mind anytime."*

"Are you all deaf?" Uncle Marvin asks. "Now I want a little peace and quiet. The adults at the table have important things to discuss and it would do you kids good to listen and learn."

"Bullshit," Two complains. *"These 'adults' wouldn't recognize an important issue if it walked up and bit them in the ass."*

"Two's right," One adds. *"They haven't seen the obvious. They haven't figured out that you have a special destiny. How blind can they be?"*

"Stop it! Just stop."

My eyes are drawn to the table centerpiece, a cut glass bowl Mildred had inherited from her mother. Mildred had cherished it and I wonder how she'd feel about it being used in her absence. As I stare at the bowl, it begins to glow like the yellow vase in the hospital. Suddenly it's cold, as if Mildred's spirit has entered the room to accuse us all.

"I wonder where Mr. Grimmes is going to end up," Marvin continues. "It's a shame. This new pastor, Merrick, closing the school and sending such an excellent teacher packing, that's what I mean. Redeemer will never be the same."

"When I think of all the hours I've spent working on that school building, it makes me sick," Father complains. "I might as well have spent my time working at the store."

Why doesn't Father spend the time with me? Aren't I worthy of his time and attention?

"Your father's not going to spend any time with you," Three growls. *"We've told you. He loves the store a lot more than he does you."*

"It's all Mrs. Voelcker's fault," Marvin continues. "She not only drove Mr. Grimmes out with her gossip, but made it impossible for Reverend Voelcker to continue as pastor."

"Dad," Linda says. "Will you make Gary stop talking with his mouth full? It's disgusting."

"Damn it!" Marvin barks. "That's enough! If you kids don't respect your elders and stay quiet so we can talk, there'll be no firecrackers next year."

The room goes completely silent. No one moves.

"What do I care?" I exclaim without thinking. "My dad's afraid I'll get hurt and won't let me set off any fireworks anyway."

Everyone turns to stare at me. It's clear from the expressions on my cousins' faces that they think I've made a major blunder. My eyes go to my father. He looks surprised, even hurt.

Hugh breaks into my thoughts: "Our mission from God is the most important thing. Until it's complete, we are going to be very busy. Does it matter if our father loves us or spends time with us? Will it affect the success of our mission?"

I am stunned. It's a cold, hard thing for Hugh to say.

"Let's get something straight," Hugh adds. "We must do whatever our mission requires. Everything else is of secondary importance."

"I understand, but..."

"I'm trying to preserve us. It doesn't help when you spend your time worrying about your father instead of what's before us."

I remember Hugh's earlier observation that there could be casualties as a consequence of our mission. Is my relationship with my family going to be one of those?

"As for you, Marvin," Aunt Bea says, "we've talked about swearing in front of the children."

I wonder if Aunt Bea thinks it all right for Marvin to swear when we kids aren't present.

"We've been trying to tell you they're all hypocrites," **Three interjects.**

"Break with them," **One pleads.** *"They're poison to you. They'll interfere with your destiny."*

"Hugh, do you think our parents are hypocrites?"

"I can't and won't pass judgment on anyone," Hugh replies. "And I'd advise you not to pass judgment either. By the same token, I won't defend them. They could unwittingly be a source of conflicting information and therefore of conflict for you. Truth and falsehood often come out of the opposite sides of the same mouth," Hugh observes.

Marvin gives Bea a scathing look, but says nothing.

All my cousins abruptly stop eating and look at Marvin expectantly. No one moves or says anything. It is all I can do to keep from laughing. Except for my complaints when Marvin visited me in the hospital, which are known only to Marvin and me, Bea is the only one who has ever talked back to him. Even my mother is more reserved in Marvin's presence.

"See how pleasant the silence is," Marvin observes, still looking at Aunt Bea with distain. "Children are to be seen and not heard."

Silence! What silence? I long for silence. Silence would be wonderful. They all live in a cozy little world, a world where they don't have to deal with the realities of Satan's malice. They talk about Satan Sunday after Sunday, but they've never met him.

They've never had him force his way into their minds. He's never assaulted them.

I focus on my father. He looks as if he feels guilty. Usually he turns away, but this time his gaze remains fixed on me.

What does he see in me that causes him so much pain?

"The school was worthwhile," Mother continues the discussion. "And everyone knows how much work we all did to support it. Bob installed the new heating system for the classrooms and the church almost single-handedly."

"It's not your fault," Marvin says. "The blame and the shame rest squarely on Mrs. Voelcker's shoulders."

"Hypocrites," Three declares. "They're all hypocrites."

"And you know her gossip had no basis in fact," Aunt Bea adds. "It's such a shame about the school. What in the world ever possessed the woman to think that Mr. Grimmes was abusing the children? It's preposterous."

Larry and I look at each other. Our parents simply don't know the truth.

"I just don't understand that woman," Marvin says. "How can she be so vindictive and destructive?"

"Mrs. Voelcker simply doesn't know good discipline when she sees it," Mother sighs. "This all came about because she didn't like it when Mr. Grimmes disciplined her son."

I could hear Marvin's influence in my mother's words. Her ties to her parents and her family's traditions are as strong as his.

"Who's gossiping now? Three asks. "They're like the pot calling the kettle black."

Larry and I know the truth about Mr. Grimmes' discipline. We know about Billy Henderson.

"Mr. Grimmes taught children to respect their elders," Marvin proclaims, "and that's more than you can say for Mrs. Voelcker."

Billy came from a broken home and his mother worked two jobs. He was often on his own. Whenever he failed to complete his homework, Mr. Grimmes would take him down to the boiler room beneath our classroom, make him drop his pants, and then beat him across the bare calves with a thin metal strip. I can still hear his screams and see the ugly red welts on his legs.

I look up at the ceiling, my lips quivering. The horror of what happened to Billy again and again makes me dizzy and, although Larry and I are finally free of Mr. Grimmes, a lingering fear of him leaves me shaking.

"But physical abuse wasn't a problem for you or Larry, was it?" Hugh asks.

"No. Mr. Grimmes only spanked me once."

"Yet both you and Larry are still terrified of Mr. Grimmes. Why?"

"Mr. Grimmes is God's representative on earth. He taught us that we are sinners and unworthy of God's grace. He taught all of his students, including Larry and me, that we are the scum of the earth. He was always warning us that we were headed straight for hell."

"How could you endure this for so many years?" Hugh wonders.

"My only hope of salvation was to become one of God's servants like my brother. I had to become a minister like Reverend Voelcker. The only question is now that I have a mission from God, do I still need to become a minister? It would appear that the answer is no, but I'm uncertain."

"Don't they see what their hypocrisy, ignorance and half-truths are doing to you?" Two murmurs. *"They're gossiping about Mrs. Voelcker, and it's destroying you. Break with them now before it's too late."*

"No, I won't. They're all I have. They mean well."

"Because of their devotion to their Benefactor, even your demons can't see the whole truth," Hugh points out.

"Is this the truth I'm supposed to be seeking, the truth that you're able to contemplate from the safety of our inner mind?"

"Robin, this is just a tiny part of the truth, a mere sliver of bark off the gigantic, living sequoia tree of the truth."

"Hugh, do you think Dr. Levy sees the truth about our family?"

"His actions suggest that he does, but at this point I can't be certain."

"How can you pretend that their gossip," Two says, *"their blatant slander, is well intended? You're blinding yourself to the truth and it will cost you your destiny if you don't do something soon."*

Could simple gossip destroy my mission? The suggestion terrifies me. I know what my elders are doing is wrong, even by their own account.

"Are you all right, Robin?" Mother asks. "You look like you've seen a ghost."

I look at Larry. He's as white as a sheet.

Fear of Mr. Grimmes had always guaranteed the silence of his students. Larry and I knew that if we complained, our parents wouldn't believe us. We couldn't even count the many times we'd heard about the importance of proper discipline.

"Mr. Grimmes was real mean," Larry mumbles.

"What did you say?" Bea demands.

"Mr. Grimmes was real mean," Larry cries out.

"Silence," Marvin shouts. "Larry, you're too young to make that kind of judgment. Your elders, including Mr. Grimmes, know what's best for you."

Marvin said this same thing to me when I was in the hospital. Does he think all kids are stupid?

What I learned from Mr. Grimmes is that it's all right to use force, even brutal physical force, and that it's okay to intimidate others, even to terrorize them, just to get your own way.

I hold my tongue, but I am shaking with anger and shame for not speaking out as Larry just did.

Larry cowers.

"We all know that gossip is wrong," Bea continues with the adults' discussion, as if Larry has not spoken. "You expect such trespasses from the weak of faith, but Mrs. Voelcker is a minister's wife. She's supposed to be strong, to set an example, and to support her husband in every way. She caused irreparable damage. And she was so hypocritical about it, talking behind Mr. Grimmes' back the way she did."

I can't be a part of this gossip and slander. It could destroy my mission.

"Makes you wonder how strong her faith really is," Mother says.

"Who's slandering whom?" Three asks.

What good do gossip and slander do now? Can't they see

they're violating their own rules? Do they believe all the things they've been teaching us all these years?

I can't be a part of this conversation. I can't permit my elders' gossip to become my own thoughts, my own gossip.

Still staring at the ceiling, I begin to tremble violently.

I must protect myself from the thoughts of my elders.

I get up from the table and flee the dining room.

22

I escape to Ray and Larry's room, where I lie down on the lower bunk and close my eyes.

The room is small, containing a bunk bed, one dresser that Ray and Larry share, and a small secretary's desk with a fold-down work surface.

"Are you all right?" Hugh asks.

"I don't know. With the clamor of all the voices, I'm anxious, and now with this whole episode, I know I'm going to have trouble sleeping tonight."

I roll over to face the wall.

Are our elders as hypercritical as they sound?

Without thinking, I punch the wall hard enough to skin my knuckles.

"I think their being hypercritical is quite apparent," **Two sighs.**

"Two, the three of you should be careful about calling the

kettle black."

"That's not fair. We've been straightforward in our dealings with you all along."

"Give me a break."

"We're all hypercritical at times about some things, particularly if we feel threatened," Hugh observes.

"Leaving the table was the right thing to do," One says.

"I'm not so sure. I'm certain to end up in the doghouse with Mother."

"But you've begun the process of separating yourself from your family."

"I have not."

"You may not see it quite yet, but leaving the table was a good first step," Two declares. "Now all you have to do is follow through. You must separate yourself. You must go your own way."

"And just where would you suggest I go? I'm only fourteen years old."

"It doesn't matter as long as you separate yourself from these hypocrites," Three adds.

"I don't want to end up in a juvenile hall in Oklahoma or somewhere else I've never been. Besides, I don't have a cardboard box big enough to sleep in."

Hugh breaks into laughter and I can't stop myself from doing the same. Of course, my demons can't hear him.

"So now you're a comedian," Two sneers. "You'd better

get serious. We're not playing checkers here."

"Two is right," Hugh exclaims. "They are a bunch of hypocrites. They make rules for us kids that they have no intention of abiding by themselves. The most important questions are: How much of our own life is based on a bunch of lies? and What can we do about it?"

"No one our age worries about the things we worry about," Hugh says. "But then, no one else our age bears the weight of our sacred mission. Oddly enough, all this seems to make us older, but not necessarily more mature, than our peers."

"Hugh, is this the new perspective you've promised?"

"Yes," Hugh replies. "It's hidden away somewhere within our mind."

"Listen, Robin," One says, "your break with your elders must be a clean and total one, and you must make it while you still can. If you don't, they'll eventually drag you down with them."

"One, my elders can't be completely wrong about everything. They do try to abide by some of their rules. But that's irrelevant. The more important question is how can I tell which of their 'golden truths' are correct and which are not?"

"I can contribute to the process of figuring out which 'sacred truths' are true and which are not. This is because of the different perspective I provide," Hugh remarks. "We'll work through this together."

I've been in Ray and Larry's room for about five minutes when Mother appears.

"Just what do you think you're doing? You know it's rude to leave the table like that."

"Is Uncle Marvin telling you I need discipline?" I ask. "Am I creating a problem for you?"

"Don't get smart with me, young man. I asked you a question and I expect an answer. Just what did you think you were doing leaving the table?"

"I can't be a part of your slander! It's not right."

"Oh, so now you have the wisdom to judge what's right."

"Well, haven't you always taught me it's wrong to slander?"

"It's not slander when what we say is true," Mother replies, placing her hands on her hips.

"Well, if it's not slander, then it's gossip."

"Sometimes unpleasant things have to be discussed openly by the faithful for their own protection," Mother continues, "and for the protection of their young ones like you who don't yet have the experience required to make judgments like this."

"It's still gossip."

If I want to stay with my parents' church, I can't challenge anything they say, especially the minister. Nevertheless, I'm now doing just that, but only because my mission demands it.

"You no longer have a church," Three scoffs. *"They'll never take you back. You've got nothing to lose."*

I feel a chill run up and down my spine and suddenly the air around me grows cold.

"Hugh, did you just hear what I heard?"

"Yes. And I can feel the cold as well. Three has just unwittingly

300

confirmed what we have suspected all along. Like the predators on the plains of Africa, they are trying to separate the sick, weak or wounded from the protection of the herd. These poor creatures are easy prey. Your demons are trying to weaken us so that they can do the same."

I begin to shake violently.

"But Hugh, we're not sick, weak or wounded, are we?"

Hugh doesn't reply.

"Someday, when you're a little older and wiser, you'll learn that this is an imperfect world," Mother says. "It's a reality we adults have to deal with. You're off in your fantasyland all the time doing God knows what. It's about time you grow up and face the facts."

"And just what are the facts, Mother?"

"I'm going to ignore that comment. Now come back to the table with me. We'll discuss this in the morning."

"Am I being asked to rejoin the 'faithful herd'?"

"What 'herd' are you talking about? Robin, you're testing my patience. Now get yourself off the bed and come back to the table with me."

"No."

"Robin!"

"I said no and I mean it. I won't go back to the table!"

Mother turns and storms out of the room.

"Your mind is warped like the bottom of this pan," Mother exclaims, shaking a misshapen, old, aluminum saucepan in my face. She's been waiting for me. I've just entered the kitchen for breakfast, still in my pajamas and bathrobe.

Father, sitting at the breakfast table with the morning paper in hand, makes it clear by his expression and posture that he wants no part of this confrontation.

Father knows I'm going to get it from Mother. Why doesn't he step in like he did in his argument with Mother before I went into the hospital or when she wanted to fire Dr. Levy? He was quiet yesterday at Marvin and Bea's during the whole conversation, except to say he should have spent his time at the store. Is it possible he thought the adult conversation was wrong just as I did?

"I suspect you're right about your father," Hugh interjects.

"What do you mean?" I finally ask Mother.

I feel strangely detached, almost as if I'm a bystander watching the proceedings. Normally, an angry admonition from my mother would greatly upset me but, on this occasion, I feel the self-assurance that comes from knowing I've done the right thing.

"We've been trying to get you to break with your family for a long time," One proclaims. "Now, aren't you glad you finally took our advice?"

"I didn't follow your advice!"

"What do you mean?" Two replies. "You broke with your family when you left the dinner table last night and you still feel good about it. Why deny the truth? Move on with your life."

"I didn't break with my family. We just had a disagreement. There's a difference."

I know my disobedience at dinner the night before angered Mother, but I didn't expect such an emotional response the morning after.

"How can you even ask what I mean?" Mother says, waving the pan in my face again and stamping her foot in frustration. "You know what you did."

"I disobeyed you?"

"That's a break with your family if you ask me," Two interjects. "You rejected their behavior, their slander. I'd say it was a good start."

"Listen to me. I did not break with my family. I have no intention of breaking with my family. And I'm not following your advice. Do you understand?"

"Yes, you disobeyed me," Mother says. "You knew then, and you know now, that it was wrong. You're supposed to 'honor your father and mother so you may live long on the face of the earth.' It's 'the first commandment with promise.' I don't understand what has possessed you."

"But what I did wasn't wrong."

"Of course it wasn't wrong," Two agrees. "You're finally starting to do things right."

"Is this bickering never going to end?" Hugh complains.

"Hugh, you know I must protect us from One, Two and Three. They twist the truth and lie to us."

"What?" Mother exclaims, the pan dropping to her side as she stares at me, her mouth open in disbelief.

I look down at the floor while I collect my thoughts.

"I followed the dictates of my conscience. Isn't that what I'm supposed to do, take responsibility for my own actions?"

I turn to Father with an unspoken plea for help. He responds by burying his face in the newspaper.

Why does Father always try to avoid disagreements with mother? At least he hasn't just gotten up and left the room like he usually does. Of course, we all know there's no such thing as winning an argument with Mother. Yet, he looks as if he's about to object.

"You're supposed to mind your elders," Mother scolds me.

"Do they really expect you to follow them like a lamb to the slaughterhouse?" Three snarls. "They're even more arrogant than I thought."

"Even when you're asking me to do something wrong?"

"What in the world are you talking about?"

"You were slandering Mrs. Voelcker. I simply didn't want to participate, so I left the table."

"Their slander is incidental," One says. "It's the fact that they expect blind allegiance that is disturbing. Can you ever trust their advice after this?"

"Grow up," Mother implores me. "What we said about Mrs. Voelcker is true. You've got to face the facts. Not everyone, even in high places, is a good Christian."

"How can you possibly know what Mrs. Voelcker believes? Has she told you? Have you ever even asked her?"

"You can tell the faithful by the works they do."

"Is simple honesty too much to ask for?" **Three replies.**

"You're a fine one to be talking about honesty."

"What about the people in the church who think I'm possessed?" I ask, looking Mother directly in the eye.

"That's beside the point."

"Is it? Are their rumors about me slander or just the Christian truth?"

"You're mixing things up."

"Why do you continue to bicker with Mother and these annoying demons? Hugh asks.

"How do they know what I believe? Not one of them has asked me. Do they just assume from what they've seen that I've sold my soul to the devil?"

My face flushes red with anger and my hands are shaking. Mother senses my distress and backs off a bit.

"Well, we may not all understand what's happening to you, but I know you're a good Christian deep down inside."

"Am I? I disobeyed you. Doesn't that mean I'm not a good Christian?"

Confronting Mother with the kind of reasoning that my elders used so often with me gives me a subtle sense of satisfaction, but it also troubles me.

"You're just trying to change the subject," Mother replies. "Disobeying me is wrong and you know it. I want an apology and I want you to mend your ways."

"I need to follow the dictates of my own conscience."

"Then I suggest you think about it today and your conscience will set you straight. Now eat your eggs. I've got to take you back to Guy's after breakfast. The holiday is over and he needs you to bale hay this afternoon. But don't think for a minute that I'm going to forget about last night."

"She waved what in your face?" Dr. Levy asks. He is clearly intrigued.

"It's an old pan with a crooked bottom."

"What did she say?"

"That my mind is warped like the bottom of the pan."

"And all this was because you got up and left the dinner table?"

"I also disobeyed her and wouldn't go back."

"This is interesting," Dr. Levy remarks. He turns in his chair to look out the window for a moment and then turns back. "I must not have made it clear that you were to see no one but your parents and brother."

"I can guarantee she understood. She just thinks she knows better."

"Tell me again why you disobeyed her?"

Dr. Levy takes off his horn-rimmed glasses, exhales carefully on each lens in turn, and wipes them clean with his handkerchief.

"They were slandering our old minister's wife and I refused to take part."

Dr. Levy examines his glasses in the light coming through the window to ensure they are clean and then puts them on again.

"Let me guess. They didn't think of it as slander, did they?"

"No, Mother said it was 'God's truth.'"

"After all the trouble it's caused, do you still think you did the right thing?"

"Yes, absolutely!" I exclaim.

Something feels very right about what I did, giving me a sense of satisfaction, of independence.

"Now, this is an important question. Why do you think it was the right thing to do?"

"It just was."

"But why do you think it was right?"

"Well, slander is wrong. My parents have taught me this all my life."

"How can you continue to fall back on what your parents taught you?" Two asks. "It ought to be clear to you by now that your parents don't do what they preach."

"You could have decided to obey your mother and avoid all the trouble," Dr. Levy suggests.

"But it wouldn't have been right."

"It seems to me you had a choice between doing one of two things—slandering the preacher's wife or disobeying your mother, and each was 'wrong' according to what you've been taught. What made you choose to disobey your mother and refuse to return to the table?"

"It was my mission," I say with conviction and commitment.

**"Don't say anything to your shrink about your mission,"
One demands. "In the long run, the results won't be good."**

"You left the table because of your mission? I'm not certain I understand. Explain it to me."

I know full well Dr. Levy understands, but decide to humor him.

"Because of my mission, it's more important for me to obey God than my mother."

"But God tells you to obey your mother."

"Not when she's asking me to do something wrong."

"It seems to me you've made a very important decision here. Do you realize the significance of this?"

"If he doesn't, he should," Two comments. "It's the beginning of his break with his parents and their miserable church."

"I'm not making a break from my parents. Can't you get that straight?"

"It's important because I did what I believed was right."

"It's even more important for a completely different reason."

"I don't understand."

"You keep telling me that Robin doesn't know what he believes because of the voices of others that become his own thoughts. Yet, he knew perfectly well what he believed was right in this case. That tells me that Robin has a basic belief system still intact despite his demons' harassment."

"Hugh, do you think this is true?"

"Dr. Levy's correct. Your basic belief system is still intact."

"Then why do I get so confused when I think about my beliefs?"

"Your medication seems to be helping you to discern the truth in general, but it's obviously not helping you filter out unwanted stimuli," Dr. Levy observes.

"If you mean what others are saying then, no, it's not."

"Why do you think you get so confused when thinking about your beliefs?"

"It's because the thoughts of my demons and others get mixed up with my own."

"Yet you knew what to do when you had to decide on a course of action."

"That's different."

"Why is it different?"

"I'm doing something. I'm not just thinking about everything I believe and I'm not trying to make sense of it all. I'm just taking action based on simple rules."

"Precisely! You're able to take specific actions in accordance with your beliefs, but when thinking about your belief system as a whole you become confused about how it all fits together."

"Well, maybe, sort of."

"This clearly reflects the fact," Hugh says, "that you, Robin, are a survivor. To get along in your outer mind, you are accustomed to taking action without having to debate your motivations."

"Why do you think this happens? I mean, why do you become confused when you try to fit all the pieces together?" Dr. Levy continues.

"Because my thoughts get confused by the things my demons and others say."

"I think there's something more."

"You mean like my mission?"

"Why do you mention your mission?"

"Because I'm not sure what it is and I find that confusing."

"I think there's more."

"Like what?"

"I suspect your belief system is inconsistent and riddled with conflicts, and that may be part of your present dilemma."

"So what can I do about it?"

"That's what you and I need to figure out," Dr. Levy says.

"And Hugh can help us," I add.

"Now you know why I made myself known," Hugh proclaims.

William, Maude and Son Walter - Circa 1898

23

We could all see the rooster tail of dust raised by the car speeding along the dirt road that runs through the valley and right past Guy's farm. But we can't identify the model of the car because it shimmers in the bright summer sun.

"I wonder whose pants are on fire," Jon remarks. "Or maybe, it's one of the Lone Ranger's silver bullets."

Jon laughs at his own joke.

"That's stupid," Derris says.

We don't realize it's Mother until the two-door Dodge emerges from the dust cloud as it turns into Guy and Eva's driveway.

"This means trouble," Three warns.

Why is Mother coming out to the farm on a Wednesday morning?

Derris, Jon and I gather around as the car skids to a stop at the edge of the small patch of ill-tended grass surrounding the farmhouse.

Mother gets out of the car. She is carrying my Sunday shoes and an armful of carefully folded clothes.

"Wash your hands and face and put these on," she commands.

"What's going on?"

"You've got to register at North Central High School this afternoon."

"I've got chores. We're still baling hay. Then we're going to ride down to Camden and go swimming. I don't have time."

"Well, your plans have just changed," Mother scolds, impatience in her voice. "Now get washed up and dressed or we'll be late. I have to get you registered, bring you back out here, and get back to the store as soon as possible, so don't make trouble."

"It's time to make another break," Two growls. "Don't let her push you around."

"You could have given me a little warning," I grumble.

I make no move toward the farmhouse, my anger showing.

"That's it," Three encourages me. "Stand up to her."

"I don't think this is a battle you want to start, at least not now," Hugh advises.

"Just get dressed like I told you," Mother repeats, glaring at me.

"I don't want to register at North Central and I don't want to go there. I'd rather just stay out here and work on the farm."

"I'll give you ten minutes to get ready," Mother offers.

She turns and starts for the backyard where Eva is hanging out clean sheets to dry.

After taking my work boots off at the back porch, I go into the house to wash up and change clothes. Derris and Jon follow me, tracking dirt and manure into the kitchen. Eva's not going to be happy.

The only freshman I'm likely to know at North Central is my cousin Larry.

"My class will have only fifty kids and I already know them all," Derris says, "not seven hundred freshmen like North Central. Too bad you can't just stay out here and go to school with me."

If we can somehow stop the accumulation of voices, I might be able to handle a freshman class with fifty students, but not seven hundred.

North Central High School is a three-story, red brick building that was old when my father attended. He'd been a classmate of Bing Crosby's until the crooner was expelled. Father loved high school. And then, while holding down a part-time job, he managed to finish two years of engineering studies at Whitworth College. When his older brother, Walt, left home, Father had to take a full-time job and work overtime to help support his mother and two sisters.

Mother and I climb the worn stone steps and pass through the battered set of double doors that open into the ground floor hallway. There we find about fifty parents and new students in the long line, all waiting to register. The queue snakes down the hall and into the school office.

God help me! The floors are hardwood. There are thousands of cracks. I can't do this!

Stopping dead in my tracks, I look for a way out of my predicament. The flooring runs down the center of the hallway from one end to the other. This will make it necessary for me to tiptoe to avoid stepping on cracks, an extremely risky approach.

"You're not going to make a fool of yourself again, are you?" Three interjects. "You're beginning to embarrass even us. The other kids are going to have a field day with you."

"Robin! You can't be tiptoeing here," Mother whispers. "The other kids will see you. They'll think you're some sort of nut."

"But, Mom…"

"No buts."

Fortunately, the hallway floors are lined next to the walls with a slat of wood about fifteen inches wide. This makes it possible for me to proceed, but only if I hug the wall. As I cling to the wall, Mother maintains our position in the nearby line.

It isn't long before other students notice that I remain pinned against the wall. At first they just stare, but the hurtful comments soon follow.

"What's with you, buddy?" a boy with a flat top and a face full of pimples says. "Are you afraid to get in line?"

His mother was chatting with others and didn't hear his nasty comment.

"We tried to warn you," Two admonishes me.

"I have to stay here."

"You shouldn't have said that," Three remarks. "You shouldn't say anything."

I look at Mother. She appears unhappy and begins making gestures that tell me I should shut up.

"Why do you have to stay against the wall, Dumbo?"

"My name isn't Dumbo, it's Robin."

"So you're a bird, not an elephant. Who cares? You're still weird."

Mother motions again, now apparently less concerned about being noticed.

Some of the other parents in line turn to look at her, to hear what she might say. Mother looks away. Her face turns red, but I can't tell if she's embarrassed, angry or both.

"I can't step on cracks because of my mission."

"You can't step on what?"

"Cracks."

"I wouldn't have said that either," Two snaps. "You're asking for trouble."

"Do the itty-bitty little cracks frighten you?" the girl directly in front of my mother asks.

"Hugh, I'm not sure I'll survive North Central. It isn't so bad right now, but what's going to happen to me when all two thousand five hundred students are here to harass me?"

"Just remember that I am here to preserve us," Hugh says.

"But I still must avoid stepping on cracks because of my mission."

Mother glares at me, shaking her head in disapproval.

Not your damn 'mission' again," Three exclaims. "You're asking for it."

"Three is right," Hugh offers. "We should keep the mission to ourselves, at least for a while. Talking about it with this crowd will only result in more abuse. The day will come when we can talk about it openly."

"I see," another boy calls out. "It's obvious to everyone you have a mission that requires you to hug the wall. Anyone can see it on your face." He laughs loudly in derision.

I begin to tremble. I don't like or want any kind of confrontation, especially not with other students.

"Maybe he thinks he's too good for us," another girl adds.

She's wearing saddle shoes, a blue poodle skirt, and a tight white sweater. The outfit would never have been allowed at Redeemer. It's hard not to stare.

"A mission sounds pretty important," a student two places in line behind Mother calls out.

"It might be wise for us not to say anything more," Hugh cautions. "They don't know the whole story and are jumping to conclusions. You and I need to talk over what we will and won't tell others."

"But just look at him," another girl chimes in. "He's all dressed up in his Sunday best, just like someone with an important mission ought to be."

"I don't know," the girl in the saddle shoes calls out. "He looks like a mama's boy to me. His hair is parted just so."

"Hold on," the first girl responds. "Robin's tanned and looks pretty strong. But wait! Isn't that hayseed in his hair?"

"Hugh, I'm not sure I can stay here any longer."

"You must learn to deal with this sort of pressure," Hugh responds.

"Which Robin are you talking about? There are many of us. Most of us don't even want to be here."

"Now you've done it," Two says. "They're all going to think you're out to lunch."

"Robin," Hugh insists, "you must learn to be more discreet."

"Whoa!" a boy in line about three people ahead of Mother exclaims.

"Whoa, what?" another boy asks.

"I think we've got a nut case on our hands. Shouldn't he be in a hospital somewhere?"

"Are you trying to tell us that there are a bunch of you in there?" he jeers. "That's crazy talk."

Mother runs her finger across her throat like a knife. She obviously wants me to shut up. But I think it's important for me to explain my situation. Then the other kids will understand and stop harassing me.

"Well, all of us are here, but many of us don't want to be here, so those who don't want to be here are refusing to talk to anyone."

The parents in line on either side of Mother begin to pull away from her, dragging their children with them. This leaves Mother standing alone and exposed.

What makes these kids think they would know a crazy person if they see one? I've seen them in the hospital, skipping up and down the halls, screaming at no one. I'm nothing like a crazy person.

The kids' parents do nothing to silence them. Their stares

move back and forth between Mother and me.

"We tried to warn you," Two jeers. "This is not a good way to start at a new school."

"And you'd rather see me abandon my mission?"

"We'd just like to see you make some friends, to get off to a good start. Our Leader only wants the best for you. His wishes for you are quite clear."

"Hey, pal, give me your 'mission' and I'll give you my place in line," a lanky kid says, mocking me. His hair is bleached blond, something I've never seen before.

"You'll do no such thing," his mother commands, slapping him none too gently on the back of his head. "I'm not going to the end of the line after waiting here for thirty minutes. Leave the little freak alone."

Mother's head snaps around to glare at the woman. She looks furious.

"How dare you call my son a…"

"You don't understand," I interject.

"What the hell don't I understand?" The woman says, watching Mother intently.

"I'm not a freak. I've got a mission from God."

The parents are as bad as their kids. They are like everyone else. I'm not a freak! Am I?

"He's not a freak," a third young girl chimes in. "He's the Phantom. He doesn't think we can see him." She laughs.

I'm not a radio program character either. My mission will

save the universe. They're all just uninformed. But, it's best that the nature of my mission remains secret. I'm sure God wants it that way.

"Ignore the freak," someone else chimes in. "He's obviously crazy."

I'm no different than any of these other students. Is this some new form of assault by Satan? Is he going to set the entire student body of North Central against me?

"All we need is some wacko in our class. It's going to be a great year."

Mother looks mortified. And she is clearly angry with me.

"Our Master can help you with all this," Two advises. *"Can you imagine what it would be like to be that girl's hero? She's a real looker. She could be sweet on you. High school could be great."*

If she knew the truth, I would be her hero. My mission is going to save the universe. If the truth were known, I'd be every girl's hero. I'd be like Spiderman.

"Have you reconsidered the destiny I have in store for you?"

"I don't know what Satan is going to do, but you have resisted his temptations in the past," Hugh remarks, "and that is what you need to do now."

"I want nothing to do with your destiny," I mumble.

"One, what is the meaning of this?" Satan demands. *"Haven't you persuaded Robin to reconsider the generous destiny I have offered?"*

"He won't listen to reason," One replies, his voice

wavering with fear.

"So you have failed."

"Yes."

"Then I must deal with him directly," Satan complains. "And you'll suffer the consequences."

Suddenly, Satan is gone.

The kids eventually become bored with me and the snide commentary stops.

We progress slowly, finally working our way into the school office and to a counter where three women are busy registering students. I stay on the plank that borders the hardwood flooring, remaining close to the wall, executing corners with military precision, never proceeding directly across the room, but only around the edges.

"Name?"

I decide to speak the truth.

"I have the many names of all those I hear," I reply.

"Way to go, ace," Three says. "Now the staff will think you're a nut case."

The woman behind the counter looks up from her list and frowns at me.

"Very funny," she says. "Let's try this again. Name?"

"Robin Cunningham," Mother replies.

"Does he have a middle name?"

"Yes, of course," Mother says. "It's Hugh. H…U…G…H."

"Address?"

"I live in one place and all places. I have no home, but everywhere is home to me."

"Another nail in the coffin," Three comments. "You're going to be dead meat before school even starts."

The clerk looks at my mother with a question on her face.

"2324 East Mission Avenue," Mother replies.

"Time at that address?"

"Since the beginning of time," I respond.

"Just great," Two complains.

The clerk looks at me yet again, frowning over the top of her glasses.

"Six years," Mother says.

"Birth date?"

"I have many…"

"May 11, 1942," Mother replies quickly, cutting off any response from me.

"Freshman, right?" The woman asks.

"Yes," Mother answers.

"Has he had all the vaccinations on the list you see on the wall?" the woman asks, pointing to a poster that lists measles, mumps, small pox and polio in large, bold letters.

"Yes."

"Okay. That's all we need," the woman says.

"He'll need to come early on the first day, between 7 and 7:15 a.m. Tell him to look on the bulletin board just outside this office. His homeroom number will be posted next to his name. He's to report to that room no later than 7:30."

"Thank you," Mother says.

"And another thing. Tell your son that although he may think his antics are clever, smart remarks will not be tolerated by the school's teachers or staff once school begins."

"Are you saying that things didn't go well when you registered for classes at North Central?" Dr. Levy asks.

"It was worse than that."

"So," Dr. Levy says. "tell me what happened."

"Well, first of all, North Central has hardwood floors and…"

After my regular Friday session with Dr. Levy ends, Mother drives directly back to Guy's, speaking only when necessary. She spoke with Dr. Levy after he and I had talked, but I have no idea what they discussed.

I wonder if she's still angry about registration day at North Central. But I suspect it's probably more than that. Did Dr. Levy and she talk about where I would spend my weekends once school starts? Is Dr. Levy insisting that I spend my weekends on the farm during the school term? Is she angry with him and taking it out on me?

Robin, Derris and Shady - Circa 1957

24

The remainder of July and August has passed into September, bringing colder nights and the rapidly approaching prospect of attending North Central High School.

It's our last camping trip of the summer. We ride out to the first in the string of Long Lakes that feed the Little Spokane River, setting up camp about a mile from the settlement of Nine-Mile, which is little more than a bait and country grocery store on the edge of the river. We stake our horses out for the night in a small clearing with lots of grass. As the sun sinks below the horizon, we let our cook fire continue to burn for the added warmth.

"I wish we didn't have to be back first thing in the morning," Jon says.

"At least it'll be our last day of baling," Derris says. "I'm awful sick of spending my days in the field."

"I hate riding the slip behind the bailer," Jon adds. "All that alfalfa dust that sticks to you when you sweat makes you look like the Jolly Green Giant by the end of the day."

"I think washing the stuff off with lye soap is even worse," I murmur.

The reassuring crackling of our cook fire has finally given way to a small pile of embers glowing bright red in the darkness that crowds in around our campsite.

"Only trouble is, school starts a week from Monday," Derris complains.

"And we get to spend our days in the classroom," Jon laments.

"You're going to be miserable at North Central," Two scoffs.

"Maybe, I will and maybe I won't. Time will tell."

"Since you insisted on talking about it on registration day, they're all going to harass you about your mission. This may be your last opportunity to get out of this mess. Accept our Leader's gifts and make your escape while you still can."

I want no part of North Central. Just thinking about it makes me jittery. Even as we sit around the warm, peaceful, glowing embers, my skin feels as if I've fallen into a patch of nettles. I can't get comfortable.

Why won't Mother just let me stay on the farm and take care of Shady? I won't bother anyone. I'll do any other chores Guy wants.

I fumble in the dark for my canteen. Shady neighs nearby. She is restless. Over the summer, Shady and I have become the best of friends. She never asks me stupid questions or pressures me to do this or that. She never complains when I tap my toes or stamp my feet. She's not always trying to make me over. Like Dr. Levy, she accepts me for what I am.

I smile with satisfaction knowing I'm now the only one who can catch Shady. She obviously enjoys our daily rides and seems to love it when we camp out overnight. She needs to roam free.

"You might be surprised," Derris says, as he thrashes about in his sleeping bag, trying to find softer ground. "North Central might be a cool place."

"I don't think that's likely. The school has hardwood floors and too many students."

"You'll get used to the students," Derris replies. He knows enough not to discuss the cracks in the hardwood floors.

"It doesn't matter," I say. "I'm not going."

"I asked my mom if you could stay on the farm and go to school with me," Derris says, "but she said your mother would never permit it."

"I don't plan to stay."

The farm has become a home for me, a safe haven. I feel as if I'm about to be uprooted and moved to a foreign land. Just thinking about it makes me melancholy. If I'm going to lose my home, I see no reason to take up residence in the hostile territory of public high school.

"I figured as much," Derris replies knowingly, pulling his sleeping bag over his head. "Just remember we break camp at the crack of dawn."

"You don't know anything."

"Right," Derris says.

I turn my back on Derris to dismiss his comment.

Shady and I will ride across the Idaho Panhandle, over the Rockies before it snows and into Western Montana. We'll keep moving. We'll be a team finding jobs herding cattle and mending fences.

Judging from the position of the moon, I awaken around 2 a.m.

The moon casts an eerie light. Subtle shadows seem to distort all I can see, making the scene surreal. I move silently and in slow-flowing motions. I've been looking forward to leaving for another world, but now I'm not so sure. I have no way of knowing what will become of me.

I quietly pack up my bedroll, tie it onto my saddle, and grab the rest of my gear. I have my fishing rod with all my lures, my .22 caliber rifle, and lots of ammunition. I also pack the cooking utensils we have used all summer.

"You're finally doing the right thing." Two says. "We've been telling you for months to go out on your own."

Two's voice seems to echo in my head.

"I'm not following your advice. I've just decided I don't need to go to high school. I've got a cattle horse, so I'll become a cattleman instead. It'll be a good life."

I find Shady by the light of the moon. Despite my own anxiety, it is clear she's sleeping peacefully.

That's all I want. Peace.

"Get out of here while you still can," Three urges. "You may never get another chance."

Gently stroking her face, I awaken Shady. I saddle up and lead her away from our campsite. She's restless, tossing her head and dancing sideways as she does when she's uncertain about my intentions. To the extent possible, Shady has become not only a friend, but a source of security. I can always count on her, even in the dead of night. I'm glad we'll be traveling together.

"This is the smartest thing you've done since you got out of the hospital," Three remarks.

330

Once I lose sight of the glowing campfire, I swing into the saddle and rein Shady into the shallow water at the creek's edge. It's slippery going. We almost go down a couple of times, but I'm not going to leave a trail that can be followed. After a couple of hundred yards, we round a bend, leave the creek, and follow County Road #241. We stay out of sight in the woods along the edge of the road. In the dark with only faint moonlight that doesn't penetrate far into the woods, the road seems to lead nowhere.

Now that I am setting out on my own, I feel a little fearful, so I begin singing quietly to comfort myself. Except for Shady, I'm leaving everybody and everything I have ever known behind me.

The lyrics of "Don't Fence Me In" replay in my mind and I realize that the song is no longer so romantic, so full of promise. I'm roaming out of desperation, which is not in keeping with the exciting adventure I've imagined my escape would be.

"You've got a long ride ahead of you today and we've lots to talk about," Two says.

"Why don't we just ride in silence for a while?"

"Now that you've finally broken away, we need to make plans."

"What do you mean by 'we'?"

"We're a team now," One replies. "Our Master has so much in store for you."

"Look, I made this decision on my own. I'm going to become a cattleman. I don't need or want your help."

"But we now have a pact. You've broken away from your family. We're going to do this together. We will advise you every step of the way. With our guidance, you'll now realize your great potential. This idea of your becoming a cattleman will have to give way to your destiny."

"Can't you get these demons to shut up?" Hugh asks. "I need to monitor their chatter, but it's interfering with my attempts to plan ahead for the days to come. We've got to figure out our mission and that's not going to be easy with them babbling in the background all the time."

As if struck by lightning, I become acutely aware of the futility of what I am doing. I realize that running won't give Robin and Hugh the peace and quiet they need. I can't escape what is going on in my own head. If I run away, I won't have the benefits of Dr. Levy's medications or his understanding.

I rein Shady in. We remain still in the dark with a light breeze that rustles the pine needles on the ground until Shady gets restless and starts to dance around.

What will become of me? I can't be the minister I once longed to become. I can't even be a cowboy. With all my voices, will there ever be a 'just me,' or am I destined to battle Satan and all his minions for the rest my life? Is this what happened to my grandfather and to Uncle Walt and Aunt Mildred? Is this what destroyed them? Will I ever be able to accomplish anything? If I'm caught running, I could end up spending my life in Eastern State like Mildred and Walt.

My only hope is to stay and fight, to defeat Satan. I turn Shady around and head back to camp.

Derris shakes me awake.

I sit up with a start, the rising sun shining directly in my eyes.

"Did you change your mind?"

"About what?"

"I saw what you packed in your saddlebags. It wasn't for an overnight trip."

"Boy, have you screwed up," Three scolds. *"There'll be no end to the disaster to which you've condemned yourself. You're a complete and total fool."*

"I'd love to go to Montana and become a cattleman, but not with you tagging along."

"You'll never make it now," Derris says. "If Jon and I go back without you, they'll come looking for you right off. Give it up. I won't tell anyone." As he walked away he said, "Maybe North Central won't be all that bad."

"So what made you change your mind?" Dr. Levy asks.

"Change my mind about what?"

"What changed your mind about taking off for Montana?"

"Chronic stupidity," Three shouts.

"How do you know I was thinking about leaving and how do you know about Montana? And don't tell me it's because you've been at this for so long."

"Well," Dr. Levy replies matter-of-factly, "if I were in your place, I think I'd have given the idea some serious thought. There are a lot of cattle ranches in Montana. It'd be easy to just lose yourself there."

"Oh."

"Surely your demons have been encouraging you to separate yourself from your family and the church."

"Does your stupid shrink think it's a good idea for you to stay?" Two asks.

"I did start to run, but changed my mind at the last minute."

"Why did you come back?"

"Because I figured out that running is pointless."

"What do you mean?" Dr. Levy probes.

"I don't think my family and their church are the real sources of my problem."

"Just as I indicated," Three murmurs. "Robin suffers from chronic stupidity."

"What makes you think so?" Dr. Levy presses.

"Satan, his minions, and all my voices would surely go with me since I don't know for sure who I am or what I really believe. I've already lost myself here at home. In my mind, I'm a missing person that everyone but me recognizes."

"You've been through a lot. But do you want to start working on solving your problems?"

"Yes. I want my life back."

"What if I told you there's a way you can learn to deal with your problems and there might even be a way you can eliminate all your intruders," Dr. Levy says. "But you must understand from the beginning that it'll require a lot of very hard work on your part to accomplish this."

Tightened muscles throughout my body begin to loosen. Is this a light at the end of the tunnel?

"You need to know that it will be painful."

"What do you mean?"

"Your relationships with others, as well as your understanding of yourself, may change dramatically. Even your relationship with God might be affected."

These have changed already. What have I got to lose?

I shift in my chair. I feel anxious, yet a sense of hope seems to be emerging. A chill runs up my spine. Unable to sit still, I hit the arms of my chair with my fists repeatedly.

"Are you all right?" Dr. Levy asks.

"I'll be okay."

"You need to know that the process is bound to increase your level of anxiety. But I'll give you medication that should help," Dr. Levy explains.

"Remember," Hugh comments. "I'm here to preserve you. You can rely on me."

I take the handkerchief out of my pocket and blow my nose, partly to hide the tears welling up in my eyes.

I realize I'm afraid of what's to come. I'm not sure I want answers to my problems. At least the problems I now face are familiar.

"You're in over your head," Two warns. "This strategy will drag you down like cement overshoes."

Dr. Levy writes something in my file. It always makes me uneasy when he does. I get up and move to the chair on my left. Pulling my knees up, I sit with my feet on the seat and my arms wrapped around my legs.

"There's one thing that now seems clear to me," I say.

"What is it?" Dr. Levy asks.

"My problems are serious. I need to use each and every tool that God provides if I am to succeed at my mission. I also know now who will stand by me to the bitter end."

"I can't believe he still doesn't realize that he has no options," Two exclaims. "He will be Satan's or he will be dead."

"Don't listen to Two," Hugh says. "Your demons are desperate."

"Let's hope there's no bitter end, but rather a happy one," Dr. Levy answers.

"What do we need to do? What do I need to do?"

"First," Dr. Levy replies, "if we can find the right medication, we may be able to lock Satan and all the voices out of your mind."

"Is that even possible?"

"I think it might be."

"That would be wonderful. When can we start looking?"

"You need to be aware, Robin, that looking for the right medication can be extremely difficult. Most of these medications will probably have uncomfortable, sometimes very uncomfortable, side effects. These types of agents are new. Many are still in the early stages of development and may not yet be available to us for some time, so it may take a while for us to find one that will work well for you."

"But you think that we might eventually find one that will get rid of Satan and all my voices?"

"I can't make you any guarantees of course, but yes, I do think it's possible. I firmly believe," Dr. Levy continues, "that part of your problem is that you've been taught things that are characterized as true, even as God's truth, but are inconsistent or contradictory. For you, this has created a lot of uncertainty and confusion. When they are about how you should act, especially if your conscience becomes involved, the contradictions can create a lot of stress. When someone promises dire consequences, you can't always sort out the conflicts, and your stress can become quite severe or even chronic. This kind of stress can incapacitate you. I think by making it easier to think things through, you will be able to sort through, or resolve, these contradictions.

"Can you help me with this?"

"Robin, don't forget I'm here and that truth is my specialty," Hugh says. "I've already answered some of your questions."

"I can't tell you what or what not to believe, but I can show you how to figure it out for yourself."

This is clearly going to be very hard to do. I am now both anxious and elated.

"Make no mistake, Robin, this will probably make things worse in the beginning. You may find it will eventually reduce your internal conflict and stress only to replace it with conflict and controversy with family and friends. And, again, your conscience will probably be disruptive. It will most certainly increase your level of stress in the short run."

"Is there anything else?"

"Yes," Dr. Levy replies.

"In keeping with changes in your beliefs, you're going to have to abandon the defenses you use to protect yourself from Satan and his demons. It will require a lot of courage on your part. You'll have to put yourself at what will surely feel like great risk. It will need to be done on trust and may be uncomfortable in the extreme."

I can feel my level of stress rising and anxiety surging beneath my skin at the mere thought of this. Can I do this, or am I already lost?

"I'm afraid to ask. Is that all?"

"No," Dr. Levy says. "The last requirement may be the most difficult for you. You're going to need to learn to live a lie."

"I thought this was all about finding the truth," Hugh says, puzzled. "Robin, what is he talking about? I'm not sure I agree. It's never good to lie."

"Dr. Levy, Hugh is skeptical about this. He doesn't think it's ever good to lie."

"Would it help if I talk directly to Hugh?" Dr. Levy asks.

"Hugh, is it okay for you to talk to Dr. Levy directly?"

"I can talk to Dr. Levy only if you approve. And, I'll have to use your speaking voice."

"You have my permission."

"Dr. Levy, Hugh can talk to you directly, but he'll have to use my speaking voice. We'll need to make sure you know which of us, Robin or Hugh, is talking to you."

"That's all right," Dr. Levy says.

"What do you mean, Dr. Levy, when you say that Robin's going to have to live a lie?" Hugh asks. His speaking voice is my own.

"Robin must act like he's doing just fine even when he isn't. It's important for him to convince others that he's okay. He'll have to hide his pain even when it's agonizing. Until people come to accept his problem for what it is, a brain condition, he'll have to make this lie a reality. It may also mean that he won't be able to ask others for help."

"Why can't Robin get help from others?"

"Unfortunately, there's a great deal of stigma and discrimination in the real world against people who have a medical condition such as Robin's. This can complicate what he's trying to do. If he hopes to accomplish anything in life, if even someone as smart as Robin is going to have an opportunity to do something purposeful with his life, he'll have to lead a secret life. He'll have to hide the existence of his problems, at least for a while, at least until we find the right medication."

"This is asking a lot of Robin," Hugh declares.

"I know, but until we find a medication that relieves Robin's medical problems, it's probably his only hope. But I believe I can teach Robin a variety of ways to deal with all these disruptions that will make things a little easier. But even these will require a lot of work on Robin's part."

"And if you're going to be involved, Hugh, this will also require a lot from you. You'll have to help Robin learn to internalize the coping mechanisms I will teach him. They'll require him to constantly monitor his condition, and to use all the things he learns consistently and doggedly. And he'll need your help in finding the truth, in resolving his conflicting beliefs, and in developing a sound belief system."

"That's what I do best," Hugh says.

"And when Robin's conscience interferes with his search for truth, Hugh, you'll need to encourage, reassure and comfort him. Do you think you're up to providing this support? Does this in your opinion violate the truth?"

"It seems to me," Hugh says, "that at the core this is not living a lie at all. It'll actually enable Robin to seek out and live the truth as he sees it even in the face of what others may think, believe, say or want him to do."

"Hugh, do you feel comfortable with this now?" Dr. Levy asks.

"It's entirely consistent with my function and objectives," Hugh replies. "You and Robin can count on me."

"Normally I don't ask patients to undertake this effort. I don't spell out everything that's required up front. I usually try to slowly lead them in the right direction until it all becomes apparent to them."

"So why are you telling all this to me before we even start?" I, Robin, ask Dr. Levy directly.

"Because I'm convinced you'll do better knowing everything up front and that it'll shorten your recovery time."

"Why do you think this will help in my case?"

"Hugh has convinced me. He is important, especially because of his appearance at the time of your greatest need. This tells me that you absolutely want to know the truth. It tells me that you have the internal resources needed to recover and that most of all you have the heart for it.

"Robin, you're also going to find in time that Hugh is right, that you and he are one and the same."

"I certainly hope so."

"Do you still want to do this?" Dr. Levy asks.

"Yes," I say.

"Now that you know what's ahead of you, do you have any questions?"

"Yes. Do you think that I'm mentally ill?"

Dr. Levy leaned back in his chair. Looking up at the ceiling, he blew a perfect smoke ring. As if he were talking to all of us, he responded.

"If we can solve your problems, does it matter?"

Postscript

Descent into Chaos is the first in a series of memoirs that focus on my experiences with what is commonly referred to as schizophrenia. Having read this first volume, you will recognize that it deals with the initial phase of my condition during which my functionality rapidly deteriorated. Hopefully, it will have given you a sense of what the experience of this descent was like for me, and by extension some sense of what it may be like for the many other individuals who develop similar conditions.

The second memoir in this series is entitled *Out of Chaos*. It describes the eleven-year period during which my psychiatrist, Dr. Sol Levy, treats me. We work as a team, each of us both teacher and student. During this period, I slowly regain a high degree of functionality. This second memoir describes the fits and starts, and the ups and downs, as this process unfolds. More important, it focuses on the many things Dr. Levy and I do, and do not do, to achieve our objective of full functionality, as well as a measure of recovery. We learn in the process that functionality and recovery are two distinguishable objectives, even though they are often closely intertwined. We also learn that realizing and maintaining these is a lifelong enterprise.

Third, fourth and fifth memoirs are planned. Each will deal with a different period in my life.

The third, *The Coming Storm*, describes the precursors, or prodromal symptoms, that were early indicators that I might develop schizophrenia. (It is worth noting that a great deal of research has been devoted to determining what might be common prodromal symptoms for schizophrenia, which is a descriptive term based on subjective behavioral observations, a most important consideration.) In my case, these precursors were largely hidden from public view. It has taken me years to understand the common thread among them. Of course, what I have concluded is wholly anecdotal. Nevertheless, I believe my conclusions might in small measure provide some insight into the etiology of some of the more profound brain difficulties that are common to the human condition.

The fourth, *Ain't Nobody's Business*, will describe my business career during which I achieve what is commonly referred to as recovery. In this memoir, the things that Dr. Levy and I found to be of significance, in my case, are put to the test. My resolve and my endurance are sorely tested. As noted in *Descent into Chaos*, I am forced to continue to "live a lie" to survive. In order to obtain equal treatment, I live in public denial of my fundamental nature. Paradoxically, this reinforces my basic character. In many ways, it makes me an unorthodox, more creative, and much more effective competitor.

The fifth, *Need to Know*, will describe my latter years during which I eventually begin to address the critical issues surrounding experiential health and experiential pain as parts of the human condition. I come to believe that if we as a species are to survive, it is imperative that we begin to address these issues directly. Over time, I begin to understand how to use the lessons I have learned over an unorthodox lifetime to devise strategies to improve our future individual and collective experiential health, strategies to reduce the sources of experiential pain and to increase our tolerance for it, as well as our resilience to it.

Only time will tell if all the memoirs I plan will ever find their way onto paper or into digital form.